1973

ELECTRONIC CONCEPTS: A SELF-INSTRUCTIONAL PROGRAMMED MANUAL

ELECTRONIC CONCEPTS:

A SELF-INSTRUCTIONAL PROGRAMMED MANUAL

VESTER ROBINSON

RESTON PUBLISHING COMPANY, INC., Reston, Virginia

© 1972 by
RESTON PUBLISHING COMPANY, INC.
Reston, Virginia

ELECTRONIC CONCEPTS: A Self-Instructional Programmed Manual
Vester Robinson

10 9 8 7 6 5 4 3 2 1

ISBN: 0-87909-246-7(p)
        0-87909-248-3(c)

Printed in the United States of America

To my lovely wife

Florence Belle

PREFACE

This is a self-teaching programmed course on the basic principles of electronics. Many books have been written on the subject most of which fall into one of two categories: too profound or too shallow. The author has long felt the need for a book half-way between these two extremes. Electronic Concepts is such a book.

If you are a high school graduate with a basic understanding of electricity, this book should be fairly easy for you. Mathematics is minimized and used only when necessary to an understanding of the material. Technical information is developed in slow, easy to comprehend steps.

The programmed format is easy to follow and actively engages the student in developing the material. Each principle is expanded to a depth which belies the size of the book. Each step is profusely illustrated with clear drawings and photographs.

The course begins with the age of electronics, starting with the electron tube. The history is followed through tubes, transistors, masers, and lasers. Basic principles is the theme, and visualization is the intent. Instead of burdening the reader's mind with a mountain of statistics and mathematical proofs, the material leads him into a position enabling him to visualize the principles.

Such a book is indispensable as a reference manual to the workman who is involved with electronic equipment. A knowledge of the principles is a prerequisite for the engineering student. Electronics is so involved with our daily lives that everyone needs a background in electronic principles.

This course will help you to build that background faster and more completely than you ever believed possible.

Each section is concluded with a comprehensive summary. Once you have completed the program, an occasional glance at the summaries will keep the information fresh in your mind.

Each learning step requires a response from the reader and provides immediate confirmation on the correctness of the response. This is a proven and satisfying method of learning a technical subject.

In the review section, there is a review exercise for each section of the book. The correct responses are provided along with each exercise. These exercises are designed to reinforce learning after you have completed the program.

The author has spent twenty-five years in teaching Electricity, Electronics, and related subjects. His experience is put to work here to make the job of learning as easy as possible. You will find this study very satisfying, very profitable in terms of acquired knowledge, and perhaps even enjoyable.

Vester Robinson

CONTENTS

INSTRUCTIONS

This is a programmed course; you learn by actively participating. Information is developed in small increments, and you are asked to respond to each bit of information before proceeding to the next. This is not a test but a proven method of learning. It provides you with a continuous check on how well you are absorbing the material as you progress.

A learning step consists of three parts: presentation of material, an indication of the type response you are to make, and a space for you to record your response. This learning step is called a frame. The course is divided into sections and frames instead of chapters and paragraphs. The frames are numbered consecutively within the sections; frame 3-28 is the 28th frame of section 3.

The start of a frame is indicated by a solid line (——————) which runs across the page from margin to margin. The end of a frame is indicated by a broken line (— — — —) which also runs from margin to margin. The correct response to the last frame is provided before the start of the next. Here are two sample frames for illustration.

1-1. Electronics is the science of the moving electron. Any study of electron motion can be related to _____.
*

— — — — — — — — — — — — — — — — —

electronics

1-2. Our daily lives are so involved with electronics that everyone needs to understand the basic concepts. Electronics affect the _____ _____ of everyone.

*
— — — — — — — — — — — —

daily life

     Notice the asterisk (*); it appears in this position in each frame and is a flag which signals that the frame ends just below.

     Maximum learning will be achieved if you complete the program in accordance with the following procedures.

    1.   Cover the page with a sheet of paper.

    2.   Slide the page down until the broken line is exposed. The asterisk alerts you to keep you from moving down too far. The paper now covers the response but exposes the remainder of the frame.

    3.   Study the frame, think about the information, and record your response. Learning requires thought, and the response is designed to stimulate thought along the proper channel.

    4.   Slide the paper down to the solid line and check the correctness of your response.

    5.   When you are right, proceed to the next frame. When your response is incorrect, restudy the frame and settle the correct response in your mind before going on.

SECTION 1
ELECTRON TUBES

The science of Electronics is actually a study of the phenomena associated with the *moving electron*. This science began with the research which led to the development of the electron tube. This book is largely concerned with solid state devices, but *two factors* dictate the necessity of a section on electron tubes. First, electronics has advanced to its present state of the art through usage of the electron tube. *Second*, some of the late developments in solid states have produced devices which exhibit the characteristics of the electron tube.

BASIC PRINCIPLES
Edison Effect

1-1. *Most* electron tubes are based on the *principle* that heated metal will *emit electrons*. When a piece of tungsten is heated to a specified temperature, _____ will boil from its surface.

*

— — — — — — — — — — — — —

electrons

1-2. The discovery of *electron emission* was made by Thomas A. Edison, an american scientist (1847-1931). The discovery was made in 1883 while he was attempting to improve his light bulb. Edison discovered _____ _____ while working with the light bulb.

*

— — — — — — — — — — — — — — — — — —

electron emission

1-3. A *metal plate* had been placed inside a bulb in an effort to reduce a hot spot on the filament. This metal plate picked up enough electrons to register a minute *current* on an external meter. Electrons were collected by a ____ ____. These electrons were evidently emitted by the hot _____ of the light bulb.

*

— — — — — — — — — — — — — — — — — —

metal plate
filament

1-4. Here is a diagram illustrating Edison's discovery. This was a true breakthrough and marked the *beginning* of electronics, but its importance *was not* recognized at the time.

The discovery that _____ were emitted from hot metal was the beginning of _____.
The discovery was an important _____ , but it was not immediately _____.

*

— — — — — — — — — — — — — — — — — —

electrons   breakthrough
electronics   recognized

1-5. At the time of this discovery, 1883, little was known of electrons, emission, or conduction. It was recorded as an interesting but
unexplained fact. It *was not* explained until six years later when
Sir J. J. Thomson proposed his theory of *electron emission*. Edison's
great discovery went unexplained for ____ years. Sir Thomson, a
British physicist, explained it in his theory of _____ _____ .
*

— — — — — — — — — — — — —

six
electron emission

1-6. The electron emission theory stated simply that *negative
particles were boiled from the surface of hot metals*. These negative
particles were called *electrons* and were responsible for the
registered *current* in Edison's experiment. Thereafter, *thermionic
emission* was known as the Edison effect. The Edison effect is a
process of releasing electrons by applying ____ to a metal.
*

— — — — — — — — — — — — —

heat

1-7. The Edison effect and the electron emission theory account for the modern concept of *electron current*. Prior to that current was assumed to be some mysterious force that had a direction from positive to negative. The modern concept of electron current is based on the _____ _____ and the theory of _____ _____.

*

— — — — — — — — — — — — — —

Edison effect
electron emission

1-8. *Some* relatively modern texts still speak of current from positive to negative. They call this *conventional* current, but they still *must recognize electron movement* in the opposite direction which they label *electron current*. The direction of electron current is from _____ to _____ while conventional current is from _____ to _____.

*

— — — — — — — — — — — — — —

negative
positive
positive
negative

1-9. As far as this course is concerned, *current is a flow of electrons*. This course uses only _____ current which has a _____ from negative to positive.

*

— — — — — — — — — — — — — —

electron
direction

1-10.   Current is measured in *amperes*, and *one ampere* is 6.24 x 10^{18} electrons (one coulomb) passing a point in one second.   One coulomb passing a point in one second constitutes ___ _____ of current.
*

— — — — — — — — — — — — — —

one ampere

Fleming Valve

1-11.   The *first electron tube* was a diode invented by John A. Fleming, a British scientist.   It became known as the Fleming valve.   The Fleming valve was a _____ and the first _____ ____.
*

— — — — — — — — — — — — — —

diode
electron tube

1-12. Here is an illustration of Fleming's *experiment* which led to the invention of the diode. One battery was used to heat the filament; a second battery was connected between the plate and the filament.

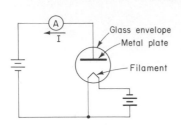

A definite current was registered as long as the filament was *hot* and the plate was *positive* with respect to the filament. From this experiment, we may conclude that there are *two requirements* for current through this type of diode. What are they?

*
— — — — — — — — — — — — —

The filament must be hot.
The plate must be more positive than the filament.

1-13. Fleming explained that his invention worked like a *valve*. He could use it to *turn current on or shut it off* at will. When the valve was on, current was _____ . When the valve was off, current

_____ .

*
— — — — — — — — — — — — —

present
ceased

1-14. Name *two* ways of stopping current through Fleming's valve.
*
— — — — — — — — — — — — —

Remove the filament battery.
Make the plate less positive than the filament.

1-15. In England today, all electron tubes are called *valves*. This
is a holdover from the name attached to the first _____ _____
which was a _____.
*
— — — — — — — — — — — — — —

electron tube
diode

1-16. Fleming proved with his diode that current was composed of
negative particles and these negative particles were *emitted by the
heated filament*. Fleming proved that Sir Thomson's theory of _____
_____ was correct.
*
— — — — — — — — — — — — — —

electron emission

Surface Barrier

1-17. *Electron emission* is the process whereby electrons break away
from the surface of a material and escape into the surrounding space.
In electron emission, electrons actually _____ from the metal which
contained them.
*
— — — — — — — — — — — — — —

escape

1-18. A *free electron* is an electron unattached to any atom but still contained within a metal. How does this differ from an emitted electron?

*

— — — — — — — — — — — —

The emitted electron is no longer contained within the metal. It has escaped into the surrounding space.

1-19. The surface of all metals contains a thin film called a *surface barrier* which forms a restraining wall to prevent electrons from escaping freely. Electrons are retained in metal by a _____ _____.

*

— — — — — — — — — — — —

surface barrier

1-20. Work is required to *lift* an electron through the surface barrier. The *quantity* of work is determined by the type of metal, and it is called the *work function* of that metal. The work function of tungsten is the work required to force an _____ through its _____ _____.

*

— — — — — — — — — — — —

electron
surface barrier

1-21. *Work function* is measured in electron-volts. *One electron volt* is the energy acquired by an electron when it is accelerated through a potential of one volt. When a free electron acquires energy equal to the work function of that metal, the electron breaks through the surface barrier and escapes from the metal. The number of electron-volts needed to free an electron is a measure of the _____ _____ of that metal.
*

— — — — — — — — — — — — — —

work function

TYPES OF EMISSION

1-22. Energy can be passed to electrons by *heat, light, collision,* and *electric fields* to name a few. In thermionic emission, electrons escape because of energy they acquire from ____.
*

— — — — — — — — — — — — — —

heat

1-23. Edison's experiment and Fleming's valve both used _____ emission.
*

— — — — — — — — — — — — — —

thermionic

1-24. Both Edison and Fleming used a *directly heated* element to emit
the electrons. The emitting element may also be *indirectly* heated.
In either case, the higher the temperature, the greater the quantity
of electrons boiled from the emitting surface. Emitting elements may
be heated _____ or _____. The quantity of electrons released
is _____ proportional to the amount of heat.
*

―― ―― ―― ―― ―― ―― ―― ―― ―― ―― ――

directly
indirectly
directly

1-25. *Secondary emission* results from high velocity electrons striking a metal and knocking other electrons from the surface. This is
always present to some extent with thermionic emission, and some tubes
use this type of emission exclusively. Electrons can be driven from
a material through energy acquired from _____. Such a release of
electrons is _____ _____.
*

―― ―― ―― ―― ―― ―― ―― ―― ―― ―― ――

collision
secondary emission

1-26. Strong electric fields can be used to pull electrons through
the surface barrier. This process is *field emission*. In this process,
_____ are ripped from the surface by _____ fields.
*

―― ―― ―― ―― ―― ―― ―― ―― ―― ―― ――

electrons
electric

1-27.   Light rays can *release* electrons when they strike photosensitive materials.   This process is called *photo emission*.   In photo
emission, the electrons acquire energy directly from _____.
*

___ ___ ___ ___ ___ ___ ___ ___ ___ ___ ___ ___ ___

light

___

1-28.   *All four* types of emission previously described are used in
electron tubes.   Name the four types.
*

___ ___ ___ ___ ___ ___ ___ ___ ___ ___ ___ ___ ___

Thermionic
Secondary
Field
Photo

___

1-29.   For electron tube application, *thermionic emission* is the most
important, but regardless of the type of emission, the emitting
material must be especially manufactured   to release sufficient
electrons with optimum use of energy.   All materials _____ electrons
when heated, but special materials are required for an optimum ratio
of electrons _____ to energy ____.
*

___ ___ ___ ___ ___ ___ ___ ___ ___ ___ ___ ___ ___

release
released
used

1-30. Let's narrow our discussion to thermionic emission. Materials
that emit *sufficient electrons at reasonable temperatures* are the
prime requirement for thermionic emitters. Thermionic emitters must
emit _____ electrons at a _____ temperature.
*
— — — — — — — — — — — — — —

sufficient
reasonable

1-31. For practical application, the emitter of an electron tube
must be able to withstand *high temperatures, intense electric fields,
strong mechanical shocks* and *severe vibrations*. The electron tube
emitter must be able to withstand a lot of punishment as well as being
a good _____ of electrons.
*
— — — — — — — — — — — — — —

emitter

1-32. An electron tube emitter is subject to high _____ ,
strong electric _____ , vibrations, and mechanical _____ .
*
— — — — — — — — — — — — — —

temperatures
fields
shocks

1-33. Electron tube emitters *must not* break, sag, or vaporize when exposed to severe treatment. *Mechanical strength* is required if the emitter is to survive for a reasonable period of time. The emitter must release _____ electrons at a reasonable _____ and must have mechanical _____ to withstand severe punishment.

*

— — — — — — — — — — — — — —

sufficient
temperature
strength

1-34. *Tungsten* is a strong material, but it has a work function of 4.53 electron-volts. It would release an effective quantity of electrons at a temperature of 2227° C (celcius). This is not a _____ temperature.

*

— — — — — — — — — — — — — —

reasonable

1-35. *Thorium-coated tungsten* has a work function of 2.86 electron-volts. It could be used at a temperature of 1700° C. This material has sufficient strength, but the required temperature is still too _____ for practical use.

*

— — — — — — — — — — — — — —

1-36. *Most* tubes use a less rugged material in order to reduce the required heat. *Nickel alloy* is a popular emitter because it is reasonably strong and emits an effective quantity of electrons at 750° C. When coated with *strontium* it produces over 150 mA of current for each watt of power. Nickel alloy coated with strontium represents a compromise between the best _____ and the _____ material.
*
—— — — — — — — — — — — — — ——

emitter
strongest

DIODE TUBE

1-37. The *diode* is so named because it has *two* elements; one *emits* electrons and the other *collects* electrons. The emitting element is the *cathode*, and the collecting element is the *plate*. The plate is sometimes called an anode. What are the names and functions of the diode elements?
*
—— — — — — — — — — — — — — ——

The cathode emits electrons.
The plate collects electrons.

1-38.   A thermionic diode may have a *combination* cathode and filament.
In this case, it has a *directly* heated cathode.   It also may have
heater and cathode as *two* separate elements.   In the latter case, the
cathode is *indirectly* heated, and the heater filament is not an
active element.   The emitter of a diode may be heated _____ or
_____.   In either case, there are only _____active elements.
*

— — — — — — — — — — — — — — — — — —

directly

indirectly

two

_____

1-39.   Here are schematic symbols for both types of thermionic
diodes.

The filament-cathode of the *directly*
heated tube is constructed of a strand of
emitting material mounted on insulated
wire supports.   The current through this
element provides heat to cause the material
to emit electrons.   With the *indirectly*
heated cathode, the cathode is usually a cylinder of emitting material
with the heater spiraling up its center.   Current through the filament
provides heat which causes the cathode to emit electrons.   The
indirectly heated cathode is a _____ of emitting material with
the heater at its _____.   The directly heated cathode is a
_____ of emitting material which also serves as a _____.
*

— — — — — — — — — — — — — — — — — —

cylinder

center

strand

heater

1-40.   The cathode of a diode is subject to *high dc* potentials.   The
filament uses low dc or low ac.   This makes it necessary to tie
filament and cathode together in the *indirectly* heated tube.   They
are located very close to each other, and without the tie to keep the
same dc potential on both, arcs would occur and destroy the filament.
Heater voltage is a _____ dc or ac, but cathode voltage may be a
_____ dc.   Tying filament to cathode prevents _____ in the
indirectly heated tube.
*
— — — — — — — — — — — — — — —

low
high
arcs

1-41.   Here is a drawing illustrating the *elements* in the indirectly
heated diode.

The filament (heater) is a coil of wire mounted
in the center of the cylindrical _____.   The
plate is another cylinder of metal which surrounds
the _____ .

*
— — — — — — — — — — — — — — —

cathode
cathode

1-42. The elements of the diode are sealed in either glass or metal *envelopes* and appear similar to these drawings.

In either case, the envelope is *highly evacuated* because the filament lasts longer in a near vacuum. Diode elements are sealed in _____ or _____ envelopes for protection. The envelopes are evacuated to lengthen the life of the _____ .

*

— — — — — — — — — — — — — — — — — —

glass
metal
filament

Electrical Characteristics

1-43. As electrons boil from the cathode, they gather in a dense cloud between the cathode and plate. This cloud is called a *space charge*. Being composed of electrons, the space charge is negative and repels other electrons being emitted by the cathode. The space charge is a cloud of _____ between the plate and _____ . This is a _____ charge which repels other electrons.
*

— — — — — — — — — — — — — — — — — —

electrons
cathode
negative

1-44. In *order to have current* through the diode, the cathode must be hot; the plate must be positive with respect to the cathode; and there must be a complete external path for current from plate back to cathode. These requirements are illustrated in this drawing.

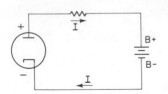

Name the three requirements for current through a diode.

*

— — — — — — — — — — — — —

The cathode must be hot.

The plate must be positive with respect to the cathode.

There must be a complete external path for current from plate to
    cathode.

1-45. The current consists of electrons which the *positive* plate attracts from the space charge. The electrons are passed from plate to battery and back to the cathode which emits replacement electrons into the space charge. The _____ _____ is a reservoir of electrons which the plate draws from to establish _____ .

*

— — — — — — — — — — — — —

space charge

current

1-46. The *quantity* of electrons in the space charge is determined by
type of emitter and the amount of heat. For a given temperature the
space charge exactly balances the cathode emission. For a given
tube, _____ determines the number of electrons in the space
charge.
*
— — — — — — — — — — — — — — — —

temperature

1-47. The number of electrons *leaving* the space charge is determined
by the *potential* on the plate. For each electron going to the plate,
a replacement electron leaves the cathode to enter the space charge.
The quantity of electrons flowing to the plate is determined by the
_____ on the plate. The flow of electrons to the plate is
balanced by _____ electrons from the cathode.
*
— — — — — — — — — — — — — — — —

potential
replacement

1-48. Electrons to the plate constitute *plate current* which is
designated I_p. I_p is also the current in the external circuit.
Circuit current and _____ currents are the same _____ and
it is designated by _____ .
*
— — — — — — — — — — — — — — — —

plate
current
I_p

1-49. In *most* tube circuit schematics, the *filaments* are omitted in
order to reduce the number of lines on the schematic. The filaments
are usually shown on a *separate* schematic near the voltage source.
Here is a sample tube filament circuit.

Filaments are _____ from tube

schematics and appear on a separate

_____ near the power supply.

*
— — — — — — — — — — — — —

omitted
schematic

1-50. The filaments in frame 1-49 are in parallel which means that
all tubes have the same filament voltage. There are many types of
arrangements in order to supply the filament of each tube with the
proper voltage. There are series, parallel, and series-parallel
arrangements of _____ to make sure that each filament receives
its rated _____ .
*
— — — — — — — — — — — — —

filaments
voltage

1-51. B+ designates the *positive* terminal of the dc power supply
while B- designates the *negative* terminal of the same power supply.
These two circuits are exactly the same.

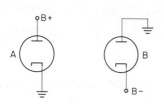

There is no electrical difference between B+
to the _____ and B- to the _____ .

*

— — — — — — — — — — — — — —

plate

cathode

Plate Current vs Plate Voltage

1-52. We previously stated that the amount of I_p was determined by
the plate potential. To be more specific, I_p is *directly proportional*
to E_p where E_p is the voltage between the plate and the cathode. *All
tube potentials* are taken with respect to the *cathode*, and E_p is the
plate potential. 150 volts E_p indicates that the plate is 150 volts
more positive than the _____ . When E_p is varied, I_p will vary in
a _____ proportion.

*

— — — — — — — — — — — — — —

cathode

direct

1-53. The diode is effectively a *variable* resistor. When the plate is less positive than the cathode, the resistance is *open* and there is no current. When E_p becomes positive, current becomes evident. As E_p goes more positive, I_p increases. This means that the internal resistance of the tube varies *inversely* with E_p. This drawing illustrates these facts.

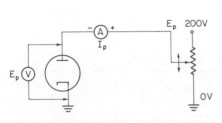

When the arm of the potentiometer is set to zero, E_p is _____ , I_p is _____ , and tube resistance is equivalent to an _____ circuit.

*

— — — — — — — — — — — —

zero

zero

open

1-54. In frame 1-53, as the arm moves from zero toward 200 volts, E_p _____ , I_p _____ , and the tube resistance _____ .

*

— — — — — — — — — — — —

increases

increases

decreases

1-55. Here is a chart showing the *relationship* of plate voltage and plate current.

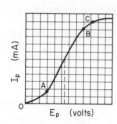

From 0 to point A, I_p increases *slowly*. From A to B, there is a *linear* increase of I_p with E_p. From B to C, I_p is still increasing but at a *lower* rate. After point C, E_p has practically *no effect* on I_p. The exact amount of E_p and I_p at various points is determined by the type of diode. This chart is representative of all _____, but the quantitative relation between E_p and I_p is set by the _____ of diode.

*

— — — — — — — — — — — — —

diodes

type

_____

1-56. In frame 1-55, the increase in current is *leveling off* from point B to point C due to a *depletion* in the space charge. At point C, all the space charge has been used for I_p, and electrons are passing directly from cathode to plate. Further increasing of E_p does not change I_p because there are no more available electrons. Point C is the *saturation point*. The diode is saturated when all emitted electrons are being _____ by the plate.

*

— — — — — — — — — — — — —

collected

_____

1-57.   Saturation is frequently called *plate saturation*. This is a misleading term. The plate is *capable* of handling more current, but the supply of electrons has been *exhausted*. The saturation point is determined by the quantity of electrons in the space charge which in turn is determined by the type of _____ and the amount of _____.

*

— — — — — — — — — — — —

emitter

heat

1-58.   The saturation point of a particular tube *could be* changed by changing the amount of heat. This *is not* a good procedure because this would be operating with something other than the rated filament voltage. When a tube is operated at its rated filament voltage, the _____ point remains a fixed value.

*

— — — — — — — — — — — —

saturation

Plate Resistance

1-59. Not only is the diode a variable resistor, it offers *one* resistance to dc and *another* to ac. This is important because most tubes are powered by dc but are used to process ac signals. Both resistances are called *plate resistance*. R_p designates dc plate resistance while r_p designates ac plate resistance. The opposition to dc is ___ plate resistance designated by ___. The opposition to ac is ___ plate resistance designated by   .

*

— — — — — — — — — — — — — — — —

dc

R_p

ac

r_p

1-60. In a circuit like this, it is a simple matter to calculate R_p. E_p is measured from *plate to cathode*, and I_p is measured by an ammeter anywhere in the plate circuit.

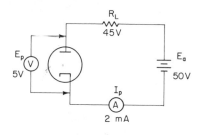

$R_p = E_p/I_p = 5V/2$ mA $= 2.5k\Omega$
Plate voltage is the plate potential with respect to the _____. Plate current is the circuit current supplied by the _____. The dc plate resistance is E_p divided by ___ .

*

— — — — — — — — — — — — — — — —

cathode

plate

I_p

27

1-61. What is the value of R_p when E_p is 12V and I_p is 3 mA?
*

— — — — — — — — — — — —

R_p = 12V/3 mA = 4kΩ

1-62. What is the value of E_p when R_p is 12,000 ohms and I_p is 5 mA?
*

— — — — — — — — — — — —

E_p = 5 mA x 12,000Ω = 60 volts

1-63. The dc plate resistance *is not* a fixed constant. Take another look at the chart in frame 1-55. On the linear portion of the curve (A to B), R_p is fairly constant, but on the curved portion at either end, there are *large variations* in the value of R_p. R_p is a relatively steady value only when the tube is operated on the _____ portion of the E_p-I_p curve.
*

— — — — — — — — — — — —

linear

1-64. The ac plate resistance is the resistance the tube offers to *a change*. It can be calculated by dividing a small change of plate voltage by the resulting small change in plate current. The formula looks like this: $r_p = \Delta e_p / \Delta i_p$. The Greek letter delta (Δ) is read as a small change. Δe_p means a _____ change in _____ _____ , and Δip is the resulting _____ change in _____ _____ .
*

small
plate voltage
small
plate current

1-65. What is the ac plate resistance when a plate *voltage change* of 2 volts causes a plate *current change* of 4 mA?
*

r_p = 2V/4 mA = 500Ω.

1-66. The curve in frame 1-55 was taken from a diode *without* a plate
load resistor. This is a *static* condition. When a plate load is
added, the situation becomes *dynamic,* and the curve changes somewhat.
Static characteristics are published by the manufacturer for each
tube. The *dynamic characteristics,* how the tube reacts in a particular circuit, are measured and plotted by the circuit designer. A
_____ characteristic curve is plotted from a circuit without a
plate load resistor. The _____ curve is plotted with a plate
load resistor.
*

— — — — — — — — — — — — — —

static
dynamic

RECTIFICATION

1-67. The diode's principal use is *rectification*; a process of converting ac to pulsating dc. The diode is ideal for this purpose
because it allows current in *only one* direction and that only when
the plate is positive. The process of converting ac to pulsating
dc is _____ .
*

— — — — — — — — — — — — — —

rectification

1-68. What characteristics of the diode make it an ideal rectifier?
*

— — — — — — — — — — — — — —

It conducts only when the plate is positive and permits current in
only one direction.

1-69. This diode is being used as a *rectifier*.

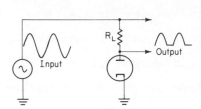

Each *positive alternation* of the input makes the plate positive. Resulting plate current developes the wave shape across R_L. Each *negative alternation* makes the plate negative, and shuts off the current. With no plate current, there is no output across the resistor. Thus, the continuous ac input is changed to a continuous chain of positive pulses. In this rectifier, each _____ alternation is passed and each _____ alternation is eliminated.
*

— — — — — — — — — — — — — —

positive
negative

1-70. The rectified output qualifies as dc because the current is in a _____ direction. It is called pulsating dc because the current is _____ amplitude.
*

— — — — — — — — — — — — — —

constant
changing

1-71. Diodes are *rated* for maximum current, maximum average current, and peak inverse voltage. None of these rated values should be exceeded. The *peak inverse voltage* rating is the maximum safe negative voltage that can be applied to the plate when the tube is cut off. Exceeding this value can cause an arc from plate to cathode which will destroy the tube. The ratings of a diode are _____ current, maximum _____ current, and peak _____ _____ .
*

— — — — — — — — — — — — — — — — —

maximum
average
inverse voltage

TRIODE TUBES

1-72. The triode tube was invented in 1907 when Lee DeForest added a *wire mesh* between the cathode and plate of a diode. This mesh was called a *grid*, and because it controlled the current from cathode to plate, it became known as the *control grid*. The triode contains three active elements: cathode, plate, and _____ .
*

— — — — — — — — — — — — — — — — —

grid

1-73. The grid exerts a strong _____ on current, and for this reason, it is called a _____ _____ .
*

— — — — — — — — — — — — — — — — —

control
control grid

32

1-74. The grid may be either a wire *mesh* or a wire *helix*. In either case, it surrounds the cathode and is closer to the cathode than it is to the plate. This drawing shows both the physical structure and schematic symbol for a triode.

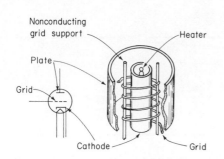

In this drawing the grid is a _____ wound around the _____ on insulated supports.

*

— — — — — — — — — — — —

helix
cathode

1-75. The schematic symbol shows the grid as a _____ line located between plate and _____ .

*

— — — — — — — — — — — —

broken
cathode

1-76. Since *all* electrons that reach the plate must pass *through* the grid openings, a *small* potential on the grid exerts a *strong* influence on plate current. In fact, a relatively small variation of grid voltage can drive the tube all the way from *cut off to saturation*. The _____ exerts absolute control over plate _____ because of its _____ between plate and cathode.

*
— — — — — — — — — — — — — —

grid
current
position

1-77. The grid *does not* emit electrons. Its control is entirely the influence of a *potential*. The grid controls current by a _____ , and it is not an _____ of electrons.

*
— — — — — — — — — — — — — —

potential
emitter

Zero Grid Voltage

1-78. *Grid voltage* is measured from grid to cathode and is symbolized by E_g. Zero E_g means that the grid has the _____ potential as the _____ .

*
— — — — — — — — — — — — — —

same
cathode

1-79. When E_g = 0V, the grid is a *neutral* element and the triode functions as a diode. This condition is illustrated in this drawing.

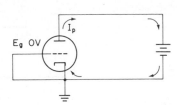

This triode is functioning as a _____.

The grid is _____ and I_p is proportional to ____.

*

— — — — — — — — — — — —

diode

neutral

E_p

Positive Grid Voltage

1-80. A *positive grid* will draw current from the tube as shown in this diagram.

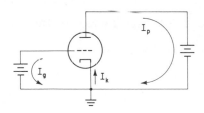

In comparison to I_p, the *grid current* (I_g) is very small. Normally, *cathode current* (I_k) is the same as I_p, but with a positive grid, the three currents are different; $I_k = I_p + I_g$. The cathode emits the *total* current which includes ____ and ____ .

*

— — — — — — — — — — — — —

I_g

I_p

1-81. A tube with a positive grid has *no space charge*. This means
that the tube is _____ .
*
— — — — — — — — — — — — — —

saturated

1-82. A tube with 150V on the cathode and 151V on the grid has a
_____ grid condition. It is _____ and the grid is drawing
_____ .
*
— — — — — — — — — — — — — —

positive
saturated
current

Negative Grid Voltage

1-83. A *negative* voltage on the grid is the *normal* way to operate a
triode. This negative grid potential is called *bias*. A small change
in bias exerts maximum control over plate current and results in a
large dc change at the plate. Bias is the negative grid _____ .
A _____ change in bias results in a _____ dc change at the plate.
*
— — — — — — — — — — — — — —

potential
small
large

1-84. The controlling voltage on a triode is a _____ grid
potential called _____.
*
— — — — — — — — — — — — — — —

negative
bias

Grid Curves

1-85. A *grid curve* shows the characteristic plate current for
various values of bias and a *particular* plate potential. A chart of
I_p with a fixed E_p and various values of E_g is a _____ _____ .
*
— — — — — — — — — — — — — — —

grid curve

1-86. A grid curve can be plotted for *any value* of plate voltage.
Several of these curves for a given tube compose a *family* of grid
characteristic curves. Several grid _____ compose a _____ .
Each curve represents a different value of _____ _____ .
*
— — — — — — — — — — — — — — —

curves
family
plate voltage

1-87. This is a *family* of grid characteristic curves for one type of triode.

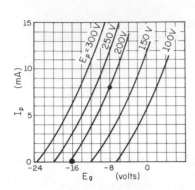

These families of curves reveal considerable information about the *capabilities* of a tube. This one is an illustration *only*, but actual curves can be obtained from a tube manual or anywhere tubes are sold. Actual grid characteristic curves may be obtained from a tube _____ or from a tube _____.

*

—— —— —— —— —— —— —— —— —— —— —— ——

manual
vendor

1-88. Among other things, the family of grid curves shows the exact amount of bias required for *cut off* with various levels of plate voltage. Cut off means that all plate current has ceased. In frame 1-87, with 200V E_p, plate current will cease when E_g reaches _____ volts.

*

—— —— —— —— —— —— —— —— —— —— —— ——

-16

1-89. The grid family also reveals the amount of I_p that can be expected with specified levels of *plate* and *grid* voltage. Pick a value of E_p 'and E_g on the graph in frame 1-87. Where the two lines *intersect*, the I_p level to the left of this point is the amount of I_p the two potentials will produce. The grid family will show _____ _____ grid potential for any plate voltage and _____ for any combination of E_g and E_p.

*

___ ___ ___ ___ ___ ___ ___ ___ ___ ___ ___ ___

cut off

I_p

Plate Curves

1-90. A *plate curve* is a plot of E_p and I_p for a given value of E_g. A separate curve can be plotted for each *different* value of E_g. A group of such curves is called a family of *plate* characteristic curves. A family of plate characteristic curves will show the amount of _____ produced for any value of _____ with various selected values of bias.

*

___ ___ ___ ___ ___ ___ ___ ___ ___ ___ ___ ___

I_p

E_p

1-91. This is a family of plate characteristic curves. Notice that a different line is used for each selected *value* of bias (E_g).

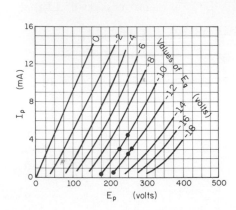

Each line is a plot of many values of plate voltage and _____ _____ for that _____ value of E_g.

*

— — — — — — — — — — — — — — —

plate current
selected

TUBE CONSTANTS

1-92. The design factors of a tube are called *tube constants*. These are such items as *geometric* organization of the elements, *size* of the elements, and *spacing* between the elements. These tube constants determine *operating parameters* and cut off conditions. A tube constant is one of the _____ factors. A composite of tube constants determines operating _____ and cut off conditions.
*

— — — — — — — — — — — — — — —

design
parameters

1-93. *Three* tube constants are very important to us, and they can be calculated from the characteristic curves. These are ac plate resistance, amplification factor, and transconductance. Transconductance, ac plate resistance, and _____ _____ are constants that can be calculated from _____ _____.
*

— — — — — — — — — — — — —

amplification factor
characteristic curves

1-94. The same formula used for ac plate resistance of the diode is good here: $r_p = \Delta e_p / \Delta ip$. Pick any E_g line on the graph in frame 1-91, stay on this line and make a *small* change in E_p; try 25 volts. Now *divide* this by the number of mA it caused the I_p to change. A small change in ___ divided by a small change in ___ with a constant value of ___ is a good description of ac plate resistance.
*

— — — — — — — — — — — — —

E_p

I_p

E_g

1-95. For an E_g of -8V, a 20V change in plate voltage produces a 2 mA change in plate current. What is the value of r_p?

*

---

r_p = 20V/2 mA = 10kΩ.

1-96. The *amplification factor* is a ratio of voltage change. It is a number which indicates the *effectiveness* of the grid control over plate current. It is symbolized by the Greek letter mu (μ). The formula is $\mu = \Delta e_p / \Delta e_g$; I_p is understood to be constant. μ is a symbol for _____ _____ which is a _____ of voltage change.

*

---

amplification factor

ratio

1-97. Information for *calculating* amplification factor may be obtained from *either* grid or plate curves. Select a value of I_p and E_g. Move across to the next E_g line. Record the change in e_p and divide it by the change in e_g. A 4 volt change of e_g and a 48 volt change of e_p is a μ of _____.

*

$\mu = 48/4 = 12$

1-98. The μ just calculated indicates that a *one volt* change on the grid will produce a ____ volt change on the plate.

*

— — — — — — — — — — — — —

12

1-99. *Transconductance* indicates how much I_p is affected by a change in bias. The symbol is g_m, and the formula is $g_m = \Delta i_p / \Delta e_p$. In this formula E_p is understood to remain on a steady value. The effectiveness of bias control on plate current is _____.

*

— — — — — — — — — — — — —

transconductance

1-100. Since any type of conductance is the reciprocal of resistance, transconductance is measured in mhos (℧). When a change of 2 volts in bias produces a change of 6 mA in I_p, what is the value of transconductance?

*

— — — — — — — — — — — — —

$g_m = 6$ mA/2V = 3 millimhos

1-101. There is an *inter-relationship* among the three constants. Expressed as a formula it is $\mu = g_m r_p$. This enables the calculation of *any constant* when the values of the other two are known. What is the ac plate resistance of a tube with an amplification factor of 30 and a transconductance of 1.5 m℧ ?

*

─── ─── ─── ─── ─── ─── ─── ─── ─── ─── ───

$r_p = \mu/g_m = 30/1.5m℧ = 20k\Omega$

Types of Bias

1-102. Bias has been defined as a _____ control voltage between the grid and the _____ .

*

─── ─── ─── ─── ─── ─── ─── ─── ─── ─── ───

negative

cathode

1-103. We will concern ourselves with *three types* of bias. These are *fixed* bias, *grid leak* bias, and *cathode self* bias. Fixed bias is illustrated in this drawing.

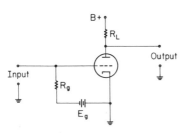

Fixed bias is a _____ potential between the grid and cathode with the _____ being the most negative.

*

─── ─── ─── ─── ─── ─── ─── ─── ─── ─── ───

dc

grid

1-104. Whatever the value of the E_g battery, the grid is that much *more negative* than the cathode. In frame 1-103, if E_g is 6 volts, the tube has a bias of ____ volts. This is the same as saying that the grid is ____ volts more negative than the cathode. The same idea can be expressed by saying that the cathode is ____ volts more positive than the grid.

*

— — — — — — — — — — — — — — — — —

6

6

6

1-105. When an ac *sine wave* is applied to the input of the circuit in frame 1-103, it will *vary* the bias according to the signal amplitude. Assuming a 5 volt bias and a signal of 3 volts peak to peak, the positive alternation *reduces* bias by 1.5 volts and the negative alternation *increases* the bias by 1.5 volts. Each sine wave of this ac signal then changes the bias from -5 volts to a _____ volts, back to -5 volts, to _____ volts, and back to -5 volts.

*

— — — — — — — — — — — — — — — —

-3.5

-6.5

1-106. The bias potential becomes the *reference level* for the ac signal as illustrated in this drawing.

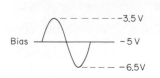

The positive alternation _____ bias and the negative alternation _____ bias.

*

— — — — — — — — — — — —

reduces

increases

1-107. The output across the plate load resistor in frame 1-103 will be of the *same* frequency and shape as the input, but it will be much *larger* and 180° *out of phase*. This means that the signal has been *amplified and inverted*. When a signal is amplified, it is _____ in size. When it is inverted, it has had a 180° _____ shift.

*

— — — — — — — — — — — —

increased

phase

1-108. A tube, connected as shown here, will draw grid current and *develop* its own bias. This is called *grid leak* bias. Without an input signal, the bias is zero.

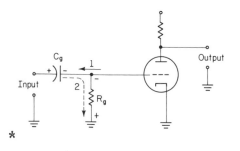

With grid leak bias, the tube has no bias until it has an _____ signal. It then develops its own _____ .

*

— — — — — — — — — — — —

input

bias

1-109. In frame 1-108, the *positive alternations* of the input signal make the grid positive. The resulting grid current *charges* the capacitor as shown in path 1. During *negative* alternations, the capacitor tries to *discharge* along path 2. Since R_g is very large, there is very little discharge. The negative voltage across R_g is the *bias* and it is approximately equal to the *peak value* of the input signal. With grid leak bias the positive alternation causes _____ current to _____ a capacitor.

*

— — — — — — — — — — — — — — — —

grid

charge

1-110. The _____ of a capacitor through the grid resistor develops grid _____ bias equivalent to the _____ value of input signal.

*

— — — — — — — — — — — — — — — —

discharge

leak

peak

1-111. This drawing illustrates *cathode self* bias.

This is a positive voltage on the cathode developed by plate current. The grid is returned to ground which makes the cathode positive with respect to the grid. The bias is developed across the cathode resistor, R_k, and is held steady by the bypass capacitor, C_k. C_k bypasses the ac signal so that only dc goes through the resistor. Cathode self bias is a _____ potential on the cathode which is the same effect as a _____ on the grid.

*

— — — — — — — — — — — — —

positive
negative

1-112. C_k assures a steady cathode self bias by bypassing the ____ _____ .

*

— — — — — — — — — — — — —

ac signal

1-113. Cathode self bias is developed by ____ _____ through the _____ _____ .

*

— — — — — — — — — — — — —

plate current
cathode resistor

CATHODE RAY TUBE

The cathode ray tube (CRT) is likely to be around for a number of years. It is *widely used* for many types of displays. Among the *uses* are computer displays, television screens, radar scopes, and observation screens for test equipment. There *is not* a great variety of basic CRTs. There are many variations of minor details but only *two* standard types. These types are named according to the system they use for *deflection*: the *electrostatic* and the *electromagnetic*. Circuits can be built to make these standard scopes display a great variety of information. These two CRTs have many *common* features. We will first examine the common features, then compare the two.

Electron Gun

1-114. The CRT uses thermionic emission. This means that _____ are boiled from the _____ similar to the action in other tubes.
*

—— —— —— —— —— —— —— —— —— —— —— —— ——

electrons
cathode

1-115. As the electrons leave the cathode, they are molded into a sharply *focused beam* and fired toward a *screen*. Pictures are *traced* on the screen by moving the electron beam. Electrons are molded into a _____ which is used to trace patterns on a _____ .
*

—— —— —— —— —— —— —— —— —— —— —— —— ——

beam
screen

1-116. The *electron gun* is illustrated here. It is composed of cathode, grid, and two anodes.

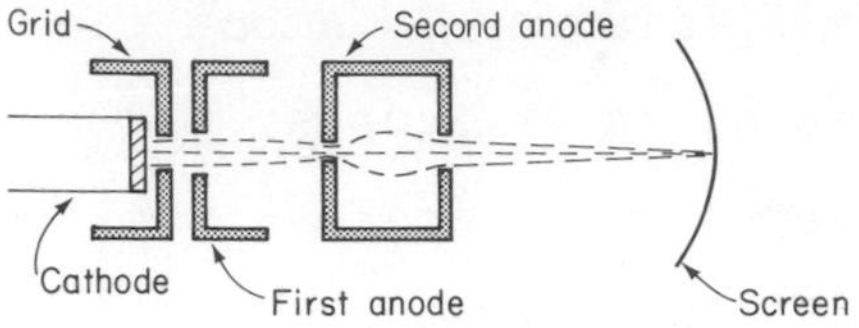

The *cathode* fires electrons from one end. The *grid* caps the cathode and provides one small hole for electrons to pass through. The *first anode* is strongly positive and accelerates the electrons to a high velocity. The *second anode* molds the electrons into a beam and *focuses* them at the screen. Cathode, grid, and two anodes comprise the _____ _____.
*
― ― ― ― ― ― ― ― ― ― ― ― ― ― ― ―

electron gun

1-117. The electron gun _____ a beam of electrons toward the screen.
*
― ― ― ― ― ― ― ― ― ― ― ― ― ― ― ―

fires

1-118. The first anode _____ the electrons.
*
― ― ― ― ― ― ― ― ― ― ― ― ― ― ― ―

accelerates

1-119. The second anode shapes and _____ the electron beam.
*
― ― ― ― ― ― ― ― ― ― ― ― ― ― ― ―

focuses

1-120. The second anode is a *hollow* cylinder with an opening at both ends. It has a *high negative* potential. The high negative potential _____ and _____ the electron beam as it passes through the _____ cylinder.

*

— — — — — — — — — — — — — —

shapes
focuses
hollow

1-121. A CRT *is not* limited to a single electron gun. Multiple guns are possible. A CRT may contain _____ or several electron guns.

*

— — — — — — — — — — — — — —

one

Envelope and Screen

1-122. The *envelope* is an evacuated glass tube with a flared front. The screen is a *phosphor coating* on the inside front of the glass tube. The size and shape of the tube are varied to fit its intended use. General appearance is illustrated in this drawing.

Electron gun
Phosphor coating inside tube
Viewing screen
Evacuated glass envelope
Electron beam

The electron gun is enclosed in an _____ _____ envelope.

*

— — — — — — — — — — — — — —

evacuated glass

1-23. The screen is a _____ coating on the inside front of the
       _____ tube.
*

― ― ― ― ― ― ― ― ― ― ― ― ―

phosphor
glass

1-124. The high velocity *electron beam* causes the phosphor to give
off light where it touches. Looking at the front of the screen, a
stationary beam makes a bright dot; a moving beam can trace a bright
pattern. Where the beam touches the screen, the _____ gives off
light which can be _____ from the outside.
*

― ― ― ― ― ― ― ― ― ― ― ― ―

phosphor
seen

1-125. A stationary beam shows as a bright _____. A moving beam
may trace a _____.
*

― ― ― ― ― ― ― ― ― ― ― ― ―

dot
pattern

1-126. The *aquadag* is a metallic coating on the inside of the tube.
It carries a very *high positive* potential. Its purpose is to collect
the electrons and return them to the power supply. This drawing
illustrates the aquadag coating.

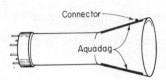

This coating goes all the way around and
is connected to an *outside circuit*
through an opening in the tube. As the
electrons bounce from the screen, they are
_____ by the _____ coating.

*

collected

aquadag

1-127. The highly _____ aquadag collects the electrons and
_____ them to the power supply.

*

positive

returns

53

1-128. This CRT uses *electrostatic* fields to position and control the electron beam. It is illustrated in this drawing.

The deflection system consists of *two sets* of deflection plates. Potentials form electrostatic fields between plates of a *pair*. The beam is moved up or down by the _____ plates and right or left by the _____ plates.

*

— — — — — — — — — — — — —

vertical
horizontal

1-129. Plate potentials can be varied manually with controls or automatically by signals applied to the plates. Plate _____ move the beam, and they are varied both _____ and automatically.
*

— — — — — — — — — — — — —

potentials
manually

Electromagnetic CRT

1-130. This CRT uses *magnetic* fields to position and control the electron beam. It is generally found in *fixed* installations which use a limited number of patterns. The electron beam in the electro-magnetic CRT is positioned and controlled by _____ _____ .
*

— — — — — — — — — — — — —

magnetic fields

1-131.   This drawing represents the *two* magnetic fields.

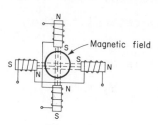

This front view causes the fields to interlace. Actually the pairs of coils are *physically separated* to produce two independent fields. Changing the current through the coils can move the beam to any point on the screen.

SUMMARY

1.   Electronics began with the development of the *electron tube*.

2.   Most electron tubes use *thermionic emission*, but there are three other types: *field* emission, *secondary* emission, and *photoelectric* emission.

3.   The thermionic emission principle was discovered by Edison and explained by Sir Thomson.

4.   Fleming's valve was the *first* electron tube, and it was a *diode*.

5.   Fleming's tube proved that electrons were *emitted* by hot metal and that *electrons composed current*.

6.   During emission, electrons are *driven* completely out of the metal into the surrounding space.

7.   Escaping electrons must have enough energy to drive them through the *surface barrier*.

8.   The energy required to overcome the surface barrier is called the *work function*.   Each metal has its own work function.

9.   Emission material is manufactured for a *balance* between expenditure of energy and quantity of emission.

10.   Some good emitters *are not* strong enough for practical use. Emitters are generally alloyed to provide a *compromise* between physical strength and effective emission.

11.   The diode has *two* active elements: a plate and a cathode.   It may be heated either *directly or indirectly*.

12.   The principal use of the diode is *rectification* which is changing ac to pulsating dc.

13. Emitted electrons form a *space charge* between cathode and plate of a tube. I_p is formed by drawing electrons from this cloud.

14. The current through a diode is *directly* proportional to the plate potential.

15. When the space charge is exhausted, the tube is *saturated*.

16. The diode has both dc and ac plate *resistance*. $R_p = E_p/I_p$. $r_p = \Delta e_p/\Delta i_p$.

17. The triode has *three* active elements: plate, cathode, and grid. The grid exerts *absolute control* over I_p.

18. *Bias* is the negative potential from the grid to the cathode. It is provided in *three* ways: *fixed, grid leak,* and *cathode self*.

19. Characteristic curves are useful in determining the *capabilities* of a tube.

20. Amplification factor (μ), ac plate resistance (r_p), and transconductance (g_m) are important *tube constants*.

21. The *two* standard types of CRTs are *electrostatic* and *electromagnetic*. They are named according to their deflection system.

22. The *electron gun* in a CRT fires a beam of high velocity electrons toward a screen. The *deflection system* moves this beam to trace patterns on the screen.

23. The *electrostatic* CRT uses deflection *plates* while the *electromagnetic* CRT uses deflection *coils*.

SECTION 2
SOLID STATE DEVICES

In most modern equipment, the electron tube has been replaced by a solid material known as a *semiconductor*. Considerable knowledge of solid state devices is older than the electron tube. The first solid state rectifier was patented the same year as the Fleming Valve. Solid states science began falling behind when the *triode* tube was invented. Interest was revived again in the early 1940s when it appeared that electron tubes would not be able to keep pace with the other electronic advancements. The great turning point from tubes to solid state devices came with the invention of the *first transistor*.

SEMICONDUCTORS

2-1. Materials which carry current readily are *conductors*; those which offer great opposition to current are insulators. Materials that are neither good conductors nor good insulators are classified as *semiconductors*. A semiconductor is neither a good _____ nor a good

_____ .

*

— — — — — — — — — — — — —

conductor
insulator

2-2. Semiconductors can be made to perform *nearly all* the functions
of the electron tube and do a better job. They operate with *less
power* and are *more reliable* than the tube. As a group, semiconductors
are *solid state devices*. A solid state device can be made to do the
work of an _____ _____ , do it _____ , with less power.
*

_ _ _ _ _ _ _ _ _ _ _ _ _ _

electron tube
better

Atomic Structure

2-3. *Matter* is any material that has *mass* and occupies *space*. All
matter is composed of *atoms*. A pencil has mass and occupies space;
therefore, it is _____ , and it is composed of _____ .
*

_ _ _ _ _ _ _ _ _ _ _ _ _ _

matter
atoms

2-4. An *atom* is composed of a *nucleus* and orbiting *electrons*. The
electrons are small negative charges. The nucleus contains *protons,
neutrons,* and *other* subatomic particles. In its *natural* state the
atom has a proton for each electron. The proton is a relatively
heavy positive particle. The neutron has *no charge* but adds *weight* to
the nucleus. A natural atom has the same number of _____ in orbit
as it has _____ in the nucleus.
*

_ _ _ _ _ _ _ _ _ _ _ _ _

electrons
protons

2-5. The electron is _____ , the proton is _____ , and the
neutron is   .
*

─── ── ── ── ── ── ── ── ── ── ── ── ──

negative
positive
neutral

2-6. The electron orbits are called *energy bands* (or shells) because
the electron needs a certain amount of energy to remain in a particular orbit. The higher the energy of an electron, the higher its orbit.
Electrons with low energy occupy the _____ orbits while high energy
electrons occupy the _____ orbits.
*

─── ── ── ── ── ── ── ── ── ── ── ── ──

low
high

2-7. Some atoms have *only one* energy band; others have as many as
seven. An energy band is an _____ where electrons exist. Some
simple atoms have only one energy band while some complex atoms have
_____ energy bands.
*

─── ── ── ── ── ── ── ── ── ── ── ── ──

orbit
seven

2-8. Orbits, or energy bands, are also called *shells*. There is a
law which *limits* the number of electrons in each shell, and when this
number is reached, that shell is *full*. The bands are filled from the
nucleus *outward*. The outer band is the *valence band*, and it may
contain *no more than eight* electrons. Energy shells are filled from
the _____ outward. Each shell may contain a specified number of
electrons.

*

— — — — — — — — — — — — —

nucleus

2-9. The outer band is the _____ band, and it may contain a
maximum of _____ electrons.

*

— — — — — — — — — — — — —

valence
eight

2-10. This drawing represents a *balanced* (natural) atom. It has
_____ energy bands and each band is full.

Energy bands
(shells)

Valence band

(+36)
(-2)
(-8) (-18)
(-8)

*

— — — — — — — — — — — — —

four

2-11. Valence means *ability to combine,* and the valence bands of atoms within a material combine by *sharing* the electrons in their valence bands with neighboring atoms. *Valence electrons* are the electrons in the valence band. The atoms of a material are bonded together by combining the _____ bands. This combining is accomplished by the atoms sharing their _____ electrons.

*
—— —— —— —— —— —— —— —— —— —— —— ——

valence
valence

2-12. This is a partial list of *elements* showing atomic number and energy bands of the atoms.

ATOMIC NUMBER	ATOM	SHELL				
		1	2	3	4	5
1	Hydrogen H	1				
2	Helium He	2				
3	Lithium Li	2	1			
4	Beryllium Be	2	2			
5	Boron B	2	3			
6	Carbon C	2	4			
7	Nitrogen N	2	5			
8	Oxygen O	2	6			
9	Fluorine F	2	7			
10	Neon Ne	2	8			
11	Sodium Na	2	8	1		
12	Magnesium Mg	2	8	2		
13	Aluminum Al	2	8	3		
14	Silicon Si	2	8	4		
15	Phosphorous P	2	8	5		
16	Sulphur S	2	8	6		
17	Chlorine Cl	2	8	7		
18	Argon A	2	8	8		
19	Potassium K	2	8	8	1	
20	Calcium Ca	2	8	8	2	
21	Scandium Sc	2	8	9	2	
22	Titanium Ti	2	8	10	2	
23	Vanadium V	2	8	11	2	
24	Chromium Cr	2	8	13	1	
25	Manganese Mn	2	8	13	2	
26	Iron Fe	2	8	14	2	
27	Cobalt Co	2	8	15	2	
28	Nickel Ni	2	8	16	2	
29	Copper Cu	2	8	18	1	
30	Zinc Zn	2	8	18	2	
31	Gallium Ga	2	8	18	3	
32	Germanium Ge	2	8	18	4	
33	Arsenic As	2	8	18	5	
34	Selenium Se	2	8	18	6	
35	Bromine Br	2	8	18	7	
36	Krypton Kr	2	8	18	8	
37	Rubidium Rb	2	8	18	8	1
38	Strontium Sr	2	8	18	8	2
39	Yttrium Y	2	8	18	9	2
40	Zirconium Zr	2	8	18	10	2
41	Niobium Nb	2	8	18	12	1
42	Molybdenum Mo	2	8	18	13	1
43	Techetium Te	2	8	18	14	1
44	Ruthenium Ru	2	8	18	15	1
45	Rhodium Rh	2	8	18	16	1
46	Palladium Pd	2	8	18	18	0
47	Silver Ag	2	8	18	18	1
48	Cadmium Cd	2	8	18	18	2
49	Indium In	2	8	18	18	3

ATOMIC NUMBER	ATOM	SHELL						
		1	2	3	4	5	6	7
50	Tin Sn	2	8	18	18	4	0	0
51	Antimony Sb	2	8	18	18	5		
52	Tellurium Te	2	8	18	18	6		
53	Iodine I	2	8	18	18	7		
54	Xenon Xe	2	8	18	18	8		
55	Cesium Cs	2	8	18	18	8	1	
56	Barium Ba	2	8	18	18	8	2	
57	Lanthunum La	2	8	18	18	9	2	
58	Cerium Ce	2	8	18	19	9	2	
59	Praseodymium Pr	2	8	18	20	9	2	
60	Neodymium Nd	2	8	18	21	9	2	
61	Promethium Pm	2	8	18	22	9	2	
62	Samarium Sm	2	8	18	23	9	2	
63	Europium Eu	2	8	18	24	9	2	
64	Gadolinium Gd	2	8	18	25	9	2	
65	Terbium Tb	2	8	18	26	9	2	
66	Dysprosium Dy	2	8	18	27	9	2	
67	Holmium Ho	2	8	18	28	9	2	
68	Erbium Er	2	8	18	29	9	2	
69	Thulium Tm	2	8	18	30	9	2	
70	Ytterbium Yb	2	8	18	31	9	2	
71	Lutetium Lu	2	8	18	32	9	2	
72	Hafnium Hf	2	8	18	32	10	2	
73	Tantalum Ta	2	8	18	32	11	2	
74	Tungsten W	2	8	18	32	12	2	
75	Rhenium Re	2	8	18	32	13	2	
76	Osmium Os	2	8	18	32	14	2	
77	Iridium Ir	2	8	18	32	15	2	
78	Platinum Pt	2	8	18	32	16	2	
79	Gold Au	2	8	18	32	18	1	
80	Mercury Hg	2	8	18	32	18	2	
81	Thallium Tl	2	8	18	32	18	3	
82	Lead Pb	2	8	18	32	18	4	
83	Bismuth Bi	2	8	18	32	18	5	
84	Polonium Po	2	8	18	32	18	6	
85	Astitine At	2	8	18	32	18	7	
86	Radon Rn	2	8	18	32	18	8	
87	Francium Fr	2	8	18	32	18	8	1
88	Radium Ra	2	8	18	32	18	8	2
89	Actinium Ac	2	8	18	32	18	9	2
90	Thorium Th	2	8	18	32	19	9	2
91	Protactinium Pa	2	8	18	32	20	9	2
92	Uranium U	2	8	18	32	21	9	2
93	Neptunium Np	2	8	18	32	22	9	2
94	Plutonium Pu	2	8	18	32	23	9	2
95	Americium Am	2	8	18	32	24	9	2
96	Curium Cm	2	8	18	32	25	9	2
97	Berkelium Bk	2	8	18	32	26	9	2
98	Californium Cf	2	8	18	32	27	9	2

Hydrogen has one energy _____ which contains _____ electron.

*

— — — — — — — — — — — — — —

shell

one

2-13. The number of electrons listed for each shell is the number
required to *fill* that shell, except the valence band. When all bands
of a strontium atom are filled, it contains _____ valence electrons,
has _____ energy bands, and has a total of _____ electrons.
*

___ ___ ___ ___ ___ ___ ___ ___ ___ ___ ___ ___

eight
five
38

2-14. The chart shows two electrons in the valence band of *strontium*,
but a valence band is not full until it has *eight* electrons. Notice
that the only materials with full valence bands are the *highly stable*,
insulating gases. There are four of these on the chart: neon, argon,
_____ , and _____ .
*

___ ___ ___ ___ ___ ___ ___ ___ ___ ___ ___ ___

xenon
radon

2-15. The number of electrons listed for the outer band on the chart
is the normal number of valence electrons for that material. This
number is referred to as the *valence structure* of the atom. An atom
with a *trivalent* structure has three valence electrons; a *pentavalent*
structure has five valence electrons. Baron, aluminum, germanium,
indium, and thallium have _____ structures. Nitrogen, phos-
phorous, arsenic, antimony, and bismuth have _____ structures.
*

___ ___ ___ ___ ___ ___ ___ ___ ___ ___ ___ ___

trivalent
pentavalent

2-16. An atom is *electrically neutral* (balanced) when it has the same
number of electrons as it has protons. But it is *not chemically stable*
unless it has *eight* valence electrons. A chemically unstable atom
tends to combine with other atoms. A selenium atom has six valence
electrons. It is chemically _____ and will _____ with
other atoms.

*
— — — — — — — — — — — — — — — —

unstable
combine

2-17. When the valence band is *less than half full*, the atom gives
up electrons easily. When the valence band is *more than half full*,
the atom tries to increase its valence electrons by taking on
additional electrons. The pentavalent materials tend to _____
their valence electrons while the trivalent materials tend to
_____ their valence electrons.

*
— — — — — — — — — — — — — — — —

increase
decrease

2-18. *Only valence* electrons can take part in current and they must take on another level of energy. There is a *forbidden band* above the valence band. Electrons must be lifted through the forbidden band in order to reach the *conduction band*.

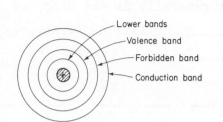

Lower bands
Valence band
Forbidden band
Conduction band

When valence electrons acquire sufficient energy, they break through the _____ band and reach the _____ band.

*

‒ ‒ ‒ ‒ ‒ ‒ ‒ ‒ ‒ ‒ ‒ ‒ ‒

forbidden
conduction

2-19. The number of electron-volts required to move an electron from the valence band to the conduction band is a measure of the *width* of the forbidden band. *Good conductor* materials have narrow forbidden bands; this band is much *wider* with *insulators*. The width of the forbidden band is measured in _____ which is the quantity of energy needed to move an electron from the valence band to the _____ band.

*

‒ ‒ ‒ ‒ ‒ ‒ ‒ ‒ ‒ ‒ ‒ ‒ ‒

electron-volts
conduction

Crystal Lattice Structure

2-20. *Good semiconductors* have valence bands about *half full* and *medium* width forbidden bands. These materials are formed into a *crystal* lattice structure. The *pattern* is generally in the shape of a cube or a diamond. Semiconductors are __________ lattice structures. The atoms have the valence band about _______ full.

*

crystal

half

2-21. The *corner* of each cube, or diamond, cell is *anchored* by the nucleus of an atom as illustrated here.

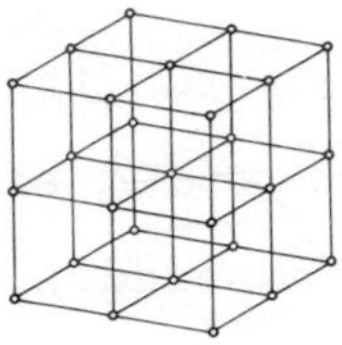

(A)

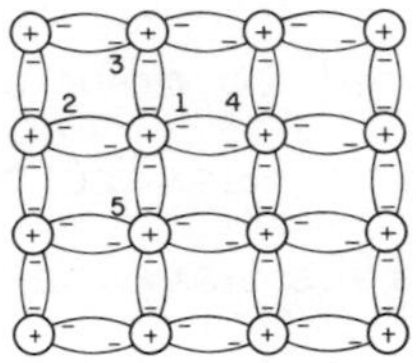

(B)

The structure is maintained by atoms *sharing their valence electrons*. This is called *covalent bonding*. When atoms share _________ electrons, the structure is held together by ___________ bonding.

*

valence

covalent

2-22. A *full* valence band contains _______ electrons. An atom with the valence band *half full* contains ________ electrons and four holes.

*

eight

four

2-23. *A hole* in a lattice structure is a *space* in a valence band. The absence of an electron creates a space which is called a _____.
*

— — — — — — — — — — — — — —

hole

2-24. In frame 2-21, drawing B, atom 1 has a *full* valence band, but it maintains this condition by *sharing* two electrons with each of the surrounding atoms (2, 3, 4, and 5). The other atoms are in the same condition; each atom uses its *own four* valence electrons and *borrowing four more* on a time-sharing basis. This material is chemically stable and would make a good _____ because all valence bands are _____.
*

— — — — — — — — — — — — — —

insulator
full

MOVEMENT OF ELECTRONS

2-25. *Stable atoms* can have electrons moved out of the valence band into the conduction band. When this happens to an electron, the electron is *free* to take part in current and a *hole* is created in the covalent bond. This hole will *attract* another electron as soon as possible. Thus, each freed electron leaves a _____ and each hole attracts another _____.
*

— — — — — — — — — — — — — —

hole
electron

2-26. Within a crystal lattice, holes and electrons drift about in a *random* fashion.

The *hole* left in the covalent bond when an electron breaks away is a small, localized *positive* charge. The positive _____ attracts the negative _____.

*

— — — — — — — — — — — — — —

hole
electron

2-27. Since both holes and electrons contribute to electron movement, both are called *current carriers*. Holes and electrons are _____ _____.

*

— — — — — — — — — — — — — —

current carriers

Improving Current Carriers

2-28. *Silicon and germanium* are widely used for solid state devices. Each have *four* valence electrons and form into a stable *crystal* lattice structure through *covalent bonding*. The two materials, in the pure state, are good _____ because all valence bands contain _____ electrons.

*

— — — — — — — — — — — — — —

insulators
eight

2-29. *Doping* is a process of mixing materials so that the grown crystal will contain either an *excess* of electrons or a *shortage* of electrons. A material with full covalent bonds plus extra free electrons has been doped for an _____ of electrons. A material with all electrons in use plus extra holes has been doped for a _____ of electrons.

*

__ __ __ __ __ __ __ __ __ __ __ __ __

excess

shortage

2-30. Doped materials *are not* charged, but the ones with excessive electrons will give them up freely. The ones with the extra holes will tend to collect free electrons. The overall charge of a doped material is _____ ; yet one _____ electrons while the other tends to give up _____ .

*

__ __ __ __ __ __ __ __ __ __ __ __ __

neutral

attracts

electrons

2-31. Doping silicon or germanium with *trivalent* materials will produce a lattice structure with a surplus of holes. If a *pentavalent* dope is used, the structure will have an *excess of electrons*. The materials with excessive electrons are *donor* materials while the materials with excessive holes are *acceptor* materials. Silicon doped with indium is a/an _____ material while germanium doped with arsenic is a/an _____ material.
*

— — — — — — — — — — — — — — —

acceptor

donor

2-32. Doping materials are called *impurities* because they alter the structure of pure crystal. A relatively small amount of an impurity can produce a strong acceptor or donor material. Adding impurities to a material is the process of _____ . Pentavalent impurities create _____ materials while trivalent impurities create _____ materials.
*

— — — — — — — — — — — — — —

doping

donor

acceptor

2-33. Acceptor material contains *positive* carriers. This means that the _____ carry the current.
*

— — — — — — — — — — — — — — —

holes

2-34.   Donor materials contain *negative* carriers.   In this material, the current is carried by _____.
*

— — — — — — — — — — — — — — — — —

electrons

2-35.   Acceptor material is called *P type* material because it con-tains _____ carriers.
*

— — — — — — — — — — — — — — — — —

positive

2-36.   Donor material is called *N type* material because it contains _____ carriers.
*

— — — — — — — — — — — — — — — — —

negative

2-37.   *Both* P and N type materials are *unstable* and the carriers drift about at random.   P type is unstable because of excessive _____ while N type is unstable because of excessive _____.
*

— — — — — — — — — — — — — — — — —

holes
electrons

2-38. Random drifting of carriers can be changed to a definite
direction by application of voltage.

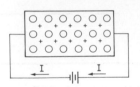

This battery is connected across *P type* material.
The circles are *stable* atoms; the plus signs are
holes. An electron leaves the battery and fills a
hole in the material. This is relayed through the
material and causes another atom to release an
electron which goes back to the battery. The
electron movement constitutes _____ and it is
carried through the material by the _____.

*

— — — — — — — — — — — — —

current

holes

2-39.

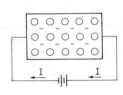

This battery is connected across *N type* material.
An *electron* leaves the battery and enters the
material. This is relayed through the material and
forces another electron to leave the material on its
way to the battery. Current is still the movement of
_____ , and in this case, it is carried through the material by
_____ .

*

— — — — — — — — — — — — —

electrons

electrons

2-40. The solid state diode is created by *chemically joining* P and
N type materials. The two materials are either grown together or
fused with some type of heat process so that they join together as a
single crystal structure. When P and N materials are _____ , they
form a diode. The joining is accomplished by a _____ process.
*

joined
chemical

2-41. *At the junction*, electrons from the N material fill the holes
in the P material. This results in a highly *stable* area with no
carriers. This area is the *depletion region*.

The area near the junction which has no _____
is the _____ region.

Depletion region / Junction

*

carriers
depletion

2-42. The material in the depletion region is highly stable. This
means that the atoms have _____ valence bands. The depletion region
is actually an area filled with _____ material.
*

full
insulating

2-43. Diffusion, growth, and alloy are the *three* basic methods of forming junctions. This is the *growth* method.

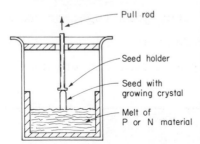

A *seed* of a crystal is lowered until it touches the surface of a *melt* and then slowly withdrawn. A new crystal *grows* on the seed. In this fashion N or P material may be grown to the other type. In the growth method the *junction* is formed by _____ the two materials together. Other methods are _____ and _____.

*

—   —   —   —   —   —   —   —   —   —   —   —

growing
diffusion
alloy

2-44. If either diffusion or alloy is to be used, a *crystal rod* is first grown. The rod can be either P, N, or a pure crystal of a basic semiconductor. After *slicing* the rod into *wafers*, the material is ready for further processing. Each wafer may now have a part or all of its surface *joined* to a material of the opposite type.

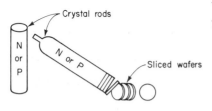

Both diffusion and _____ procedures require a crystal to be _____ and _____ into wafers.

*

—   —   —   —   —   —   —   —   —   —

alloy
grown
sliced

2-45. *Diffused* junctions can be formed by placing the wafers in an envelope filled with *gas* and *heating* it in a diffusion furnace. The temperature is held *just below* the melting point of the wafer for several hours. The *entire surface* of the wafer is diffused with the gas.

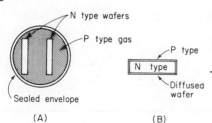

(A)   (B)

The diffusion process _____ the entire surface of the wafer with an opposite _____ material.

*

joins
type

2-46. After a wafer has been diffused, it may be *sliced* into many pieces with each piece containing a *P-N junction*. Each junction may be used for a diode. Many _____ can be made from a single _____ crystal.

*

diodes
diffused

2-47. Many junctions can be *grown* into a single crystal rod, also.
A melt can be doped with both P *and* N impurities.

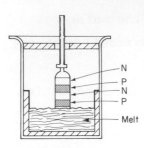

As the crystal is withdrawn, an *N layer* grows at
one temperature and a *P layer* at another temperature.
Many junctions can be grown from a _____ which contains both P and N impurities by controlling the

_____ .

*

melt

temperature

2-48. In the *alloy* process, one type of material is placed on a
wafer of the opposite type. The two materials are *heated* until one
melts and forms an alloy with the other.

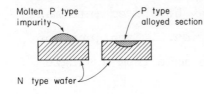

The molten material *penetrates* into the
wafer and forms an alloy junction. The
wafer is one type of material and the
alloyed section is the other. The molten
material _____ the wafer and forms an _____ junction.

*

penetrates
alloy

2-49. With solid state devices, any type of control voltage is called *bias*. Placing *bias* across a diode will cause electrons to cross the depletion region and set up *current*. Current from N to P can be obtained easily, but very *little current* can be obtained in the opposite direction, from P to N. Control voltage is _____, and it can be used to cause current through a _____.
*

bias
diode

2-50. The N to P *direction* is described in many ways. It is the *forward direction*, the *direction of majority current*, and the front direction. A *small bias* applied with negative to N and positive to P will establish an *appreciable* current. The direction of _____ current is from N to P across the _____ .
*

majority
junction

2-51. The P to N direction across the junction is the direction of *minority current*, the *reverse direction*, or the *back direction*. _____ current crosses the junction from P to N.
*

Minority

2-52.

Majority current   Minority current

The ability of a diode to pass current in *one direction* more readily than the other is its most valuable characteristic. For a given amount of bias, the majority current from ___ to ___ may be more than a thousand times as great as the minority current from ___ to ___ .

*

— — — — — — — — — — — — — — —

N

P

P

N

2-53. When the applied voltage *aids majority* current, it is *forward bias*. When it *aids minority* current, it is *reverse* bias.

Minority current   Majority current

Reverse bias   Forward bias

In both cases, the bias *determines* the direction of current. With *forward* bias, a *lot of current* is present. With *reverse* bias, current is so *small* that it can be ignored in most cases. Reverse bias aids _____ current while forward bias aids _____ current.

*

— — — — — — — — — — — — — — —

minority

majority

2-54. A *forward* biased diode is in the *on* condition because it allows a _____ current.

*

— — — — — — — — — — — — — — —

heavy

2-55.   The *reverse* biased diode is *cut off* because it allows only a
very _____ current.
*
━ ━ ━ ━ ━ ━ ━ ━ ━ ━ ━ ━ ━ ━

small

2-56.   This is a schematic symbol for a diode.

The *arrow* represents P type material. The direction of
majority current is _____ the arrow which is from N
to P.
*
━ ━ ━ ━ ━ ━ ━ ━ ━ ━ ━ ━ ━ ━

against

2-57.   The direction of minority current, if any, is _____ the arrow
from P to N.
*
━ ━ ━ ━ ━ ━ ━ ━ ━ ━ ━ ━ ━ ━

with

2-58. Most diode characteristics have been mentioned and the others can be deduced by *comparison* with the electron tube diode. Here is a graph of the *normal* current characteristics.

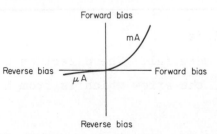

Forward current is obtained with _____ bias and it is in the mA range. Reverse current in the ____ range is obtained by _____ bias.

*

forward

μA

reverse

2-59. When reverse bias is *increased* beyond a certain critical level, a *breakdown* occurs. This is marked by a sharp increase in reverse current.

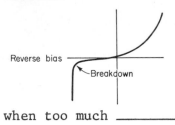

Some diodes are *designed* to operate in this breakdown region but it *destroys* a common diode. A diode breakdown accompanied by a sharp increase in _____ current occurs when too much _____ bias is applied.

*

reverse

reverse

2-60. The knee on the curve is called *avalanche breakdown* and the bias at that point is the *breakdown voltage*. Some special diodes operate in the _____ region, but _____ destroys the common diode.

*

──

breakdown
breakdown

DIODE RECTIFIERS

2-61. This drawing illustrates the *rectifying* function of a diode. The ac sine wave is changed to a pulsating dc by *eliminating* each negative alternation. Rectification is changing ac to _____ dc. This circuit passes the positive alternations and _____ the negative alternations.

Input   R_L   Output

*

──

pulsating
eliminates

──

2-62. Each *positive* alternation places *forward* bias on the diode and causes current from ground, through R_L, and through the diode. This current is *proportional* to the positive swing of the signal. Each positive alternation is developed across ___ and passed on to the output.

*

──

R_L

2-63. Each *negative* alternation *reverse* biases the diode and shuts off the current. With *no current* in the circuit, the output across R_L is _____, and this _____ the negative alternation.

*

— — — — — — — — — — — — — — —

zero

eliminates

2-64. The diode in frame 2-61 is a *positive rectifier*. It can be changed to a negative rectifier by *reversing* the diode in the circuit.

The positive rectifier passes the _____ alternations while the negative rectifier passes the _____ alternations.

*

— — — — — — — — — — — — — — —

positive

negative

2-65. The *positive* input to the circuit in frame 2-64 places _____ bias on the diode and stops all _____ . The output during this time is _____ .

*

— — — — — — — — — — — — — — —

reverse

current

zero

2-66. The *negative* alternation in frame 2-64 places _____ bias on the diode and causes current downward through R_L. The output during this time is a _____ pulse proportional to the _____ alternation of the input.

*

- - - - - - - - - - - - - - - - - - - -

forward

negative

negative

Zener Diode

2-67. The *zener diode* is designed to operate in the breakdown region. The proper operating bias is enough *reverse* voltage to place it in the center of the avalanche breakdown region.

The zener region corresponds to the _____ breakdown region.

*

- - - - - - - - - - - - - - - - - - - -

avalanche

2-68. This drawing shows a schematic *symbol* for the zener diode and
illustrates its *function* as a voltage regulator.

In this position, the dc input _____
biases the zener diode into _____
breakdown.

*

— — — — — — — — — — — — — — — — —

reverse

avalanche

2-69. In frame 2-68, *avalanche current* is from ground, through the
diode with the arrow, and through R_1 to the + dc. As far as the
diode is concerned, this is _____ current.

*

— — — — — — — — — — — — — — — — —

reverse

2-70. Any *change* in dc level results in a change in zener *bias*. The
zener current changes to *compensate* for these variations. The result
is a steady current through R_L and a *regulated* dc output. When the
input dc increases, the diode conducts _____ . This drops the
increase across R_1 and the voltage across R_L remains _____ .

*

— — — — — — — — — — — — — — — — —

more

steady

2-71. A *transistor* has two or more P-N junctions. The *triode* transistor has a thin piece of one type of material *sandwiched* between two pieces of opposite type material.

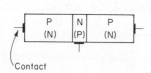

Contact

This may be a donor *between* two acceptors or an acceptor *between* two donors. The transistors are named according to the *arrangement* of the material types. The NPN has an _____ between two _____ while the PNP has a _____ between two _____ .

*

— — — — — — — — — — —

acceptor

donors

donor

acceptors

2-72. The transistor ranges in *size* from very small to microscopic. Here is a random assortment of tubes and transistors. This is approximately *actual size* which makes it impossible to show either the _____ tube or the _____ transistor.

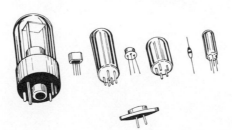

*

— — — — — — — — — — —

largest

smallest

2-73. The types have already been mentioned as NPN and PNP. In either case, the *center* material is the *base, one extreme* is the *emitter*, and the *other extreme* is the *collector*.

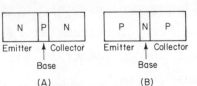

(A)   (B)

The transistor in drawing A is an _____ type. The other is _____.

*

— — — — — — — — — — — —

NPN

PNP

2-74. The *three parts* shown in frame 2-73 are standard. The center material is always the _____.

*

— — — — — — — — — — — —

base

2-75. Each triode has its own schematic symbol but the only difference is the *direction of the arrow*. The arrow is the *emitter*, and it
points *opposite to the direction of majority current*. This means
that the arrow *always* points to N type material.

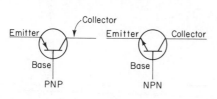

The arrow pointing *inward* shows the base
to be ____ type. This is the symbol for
the ____ triode. When the arrow points
outward, the base is ____ type. This is
the symbol for the ____ triode.

*

_ _ _ _ _ _ _ _ _ _ _ _ _

N

PNP

P

NPN

Triode Characteristics

2-76. Transistor junctions are formed in the *same manner* as diode
junctions. This means that they can be _____ , _____ , or
_____ .

*

_ _ _ _ _ _ _ _ _ _ _ _ _

grown

diffused

alloyed

2-77. A triode is actually the joining of *two diodes*. One diode is the *emitter-base* junction and the other is the *collector-base* junction. It can be biased in a manner which allows the *input signal to one* diode to control the current through the *other*. The triode is equivalent to two _____. When properly biased, the _____ to one diode controls the _____ through the other.
*

— — — — — — — — — — — — — —

diodes

signal

current

OPERATION OF THE NPN

2-78. *Proper bias* means that the emitter-base junction is *forward* biased while the collector-base junction is *reverse* biased. This drawing illustrates proper bias for an NPN triode.

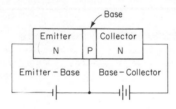

The battery across the emitter-base junction is aiding _____ current while the battery across the collector-base junction is aiding _____ current.
*

— — — — — — — — — — — — — —

majority

minority

2-79. The properly biased NPN has its total current supplied *from the emitter*. It passes into the base and is *divided* between base and collector.

The emitter current (I_e) is the same as _____ circuit current. About ____ percent of this becomes base current (I_b) and ____ percent becomes collector current (I_c).

*

— — — — — — — — — — — — — —

total

2

98

2-80. Since *total* circuit current passes through the emitter, *control* of emitter current is also direct _____ of circuit current.

*

— — — — — — — — — — — — — —

control

2-81. The *ratio* of I_b to I_c shown in frame 2-79 will hold approximately true for *all levels* of bias. The emitter current is directly proportional to the forward bias on the _____ junction and the other currents are directly proportional to _____ current.

*

— — — — — — — — — — — — — —

emitter-base

emitter

2-82.   This is the NPN in a *schematic* with input and output.

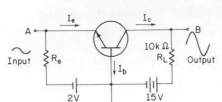

The 2V battery is _____ bias for the input (emitter-base) section.   The 15V battery is _____ bias for the output (collector-base) section.

*
— — — — — — — — — — — — —

forward

reverse

2-83.   In frame 2-82, when the input signal swings *positive* it _____ the forward bias on the input section.   This causes a _____ in I_e, I_b, and I_c.

*
— — — — — — — — — — — — —

decreases

decrease

2-84.   In frame 2-82, when the input signal swings *negative*, it _____ forward bias on the input section and causes an _____ in I_e, I_b, and I_c.

*
— — — — — — — — — — — — —

increases

increase

2-85. A *small* change in input bias causes a *large* change in I_e. About 98% of this change is reflected in the *collector*. Since R_L is a large resistor, a small change of current produces a _____ change in output voltage.
*

- - - - - - - - - - - - - - - - - -

large

2-86. The *output* signal is an exact duplicate of the input but it is *larger*. The NPN changes the signal in no way except in _____ .
*

- - - - - - - - - - - - - - - - - -

amplitude

2-87. A relatively *small signal* can drive a transistor all the way to both cut off and saturation. In this case, input and output have the same phase and frequency but the output has *amplitude distortion*. A transistor can be overdriven by a _____ signal, and when over-driven, the output is _____ .
*

- - - - - - - - - - - - - - - - - -

small
distorted

2-88. To avoid amplitude distortion, the transistor must be operated so that it neither ____ ____ nor _____ .
*

- - - - - - - - - - - - - - - - - -

cuts off
saturates

2-89. In addition to being an amplifier, the transistor is widely used as an *electronic switch*. In this case, it operates *only* in the saturation and cut off conditions. It is held cut off by reverse bias. A *small* signal can override the bias and drive the transistor to *saturation*. When the signal passes, it *reverts* to the cut off state. The transistor is an effective electronic _____. In this case its two states are _____ ____ and _____.

*

— — — — — — — — — — — — — — — —

switch
cut off
saturation

OPERATION OF THE PNP

2-90. The operation of the PNP is very *nearly the same* as that of the NPN. The basic *differences* are the *bias* polarities and the *direction of current*. Here is an illustration of a properly biased PNP triode.

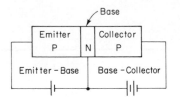

The emitter-base junction still has _____ bias, and the collector-base junction still has _____ bias. In order to accomplish this, both bias batteries had to be _____.

*

— — — — — — — — — — — — — — — —

forward
reverse
reversed

2-91. I_e is still the *same as* total circuit current, but now current enters from the *collector and the base*. These two currents *combine* and pass out through the *emitter*. The same current ratios exist as before.

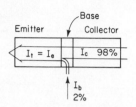

_____ percent of I_e enters through the base and _____ percent through the collector.

*

— — — — — — — — — — — —

2

98

2-92. Nothing has really changed *except* polarities of _____ and directions of _____ .

*

— — — — — — — — — — — —

bias

currents

2-93. This is a properly biased PNP in a *circuit* with input and output. The 2V battery is _____ biased on the input junction, and the 15V battery provides _____ bias for the output junction.

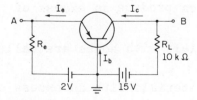

*

— — — — — — — — — — — —

forward

reverse

2-94. The *input signal* controls the input *bias* and the emitter *current*. The input signal is *reproduced* in the output with no change except amplitude. The PNP _____ the signal but changes it in no other way.

*

— — — — — — — — — — — — — —

amplifies

SUMMARY

1. *Electrons* orbit about the *nucleus* of atoms at levels known as *energy bands* or shells.

2. The outer band is the highest energy level and is the *valence band*.

3. A *full* valence band contains *eight* electrons. When this band is full, the atom is *chemically stable,* and the material is a *good insulator*.

4. An atom is *electrically neutral* when there is a *balance* of electrons and protons.

5. When a valence band is *less than half full,* the atom gives up electrons easily. If the band is *more than half full*, the atom tries to take on additional electrons.

6. A certain amount of *energy* is required to lift an electron from the valence band, through the forbidden, and into the conduction band.

7. Crystal structures are formed by *covalent bonding* which is a sharing of valence electrons among atoms.

8. Doping with *trivalent* impurities produces materials with an excess of holes. *Pentavalent* impurities produce an excess of electrons.

9. *Holes are positive carriers,* and materials with holes are called P type materials.

10. *Electrons are negative carriers,* and materials with an excess of electrons are called N type materials.

11. P type materials are *acceptors,* and N type materials are *donors*.

12. In the P type material, current is carried by the *holes*. In the N type, current is carried by *electrons*.

13. A solid state diode is formed by *chemically joining* P and N materials.

14. An area near the junction has *no carriers*. The material in this area is *stable*, and the area is called the *depletion region*.

15. A battery connected with + to P and – to N will *aid* the *majority* (forward) current. This is *forward* bias.

16. A battery connected with + to N and – to P will *aid minority* (reverse) current. This is *reverse* bias.

17. A diode with *forward* bias has a *heavy* current. With *reverse* bias, it has *very little* or no current.

18. *Avalanche breakdown* occurs when too much reverse bias is applied to a diode. The *zener* diode operates in the breakdown region, but it destroys common diodes.

19. A *triode transistor* has a thin layer of one type of material between two sections of opposite type material.

20. The NPN has an N type *emitter*, a P type *base*, and an N type *collector*.

21. The PNP has a P type emitter, an N type base, and a P type collector.

22. On the schematic symbol, the element with the arrow is the *emitter*. The arrow *always* points toward N type material, and majority current flows *against* the arrow.

23. The *two junctions* in a triode are equivalent to two diodes. When properly biased, the signal *input* to one junction *controls the current* through the other.

24. Proper bias is *forward* bias on the *emitter-base* junction and *reverse* bias on the *collector-base* junction.

25. Emitter current is the same as *total circuit current*. The base current is about 2% of I_e and the other 98% is collector current.

26. The output is a reproduction of the input with a *higher* amplitude.

27. When used as a *switch*, the transistor operates at cut off and saturation.

SECTION 3
POWER CONVERSION

Power is one thing that is *common* to all electronic equipment. No matter how sophisticated the system may become, the power supply will be there in some form. Over the years, power requirements have been reduced, but the need is just as real as it ever was.

CONVERSION UNITS

3-1. There are *many sources* of electric energy, but the battery and generator have been the most *practical*. Despite their popularity, the raw output from these sources is *seldom suited* to the specific need. Power *conversion units* of some type are necessary in nearly *all* equipment. The most popular sources of electric energy are

_____ and _____ .

*

— — — — — — — — — — — — — — —

batteries
generators

3-2. In most cases, some type of _____ _____ unit is necessary to provide the proper voltage.

*

— — — — — — — — — — — — — — —

power conversion

3-3. Some of the *tasks* performed by conversion units are changing ac to dc, dc to ac, low ac to high ac, high ac to low ac, low dc to high dc, and high dc to low dc. Power conversion units are used to provide the _____ and _____ of the voltage needed.
*

— — — — — — — — — — — — — —

type
amplitude

The Dynamotor

3-4. The *dynamotor* is used to either increase or decrease the amplitude of a dc voltage. It is a combination dc *motor and generator*. This is a drawing of a small dynamotor.

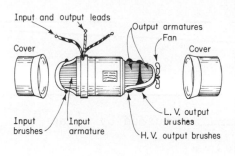

A dc input turns the motor which is on the same shaft as the generator. The generator provides a *choice* of outputs. The *low* output is a dc which is lower in amplitude than the input dc. The *high* output is a dc which is greater in amplitude than the input dc. The dynamotor is a conversion unit which changes the _____ of a dc voltage. The output can be either higher or lower than the _____.
*

— — — — — — — — — — — — — —

amplitude
input

3-5. The dynamotor is a combination dc _____ and _____ .
It has a _____ input and a _____ output.
*

— — — — — — — — — — — — — —

motor

generator

dc

dc

The Rotary Converter

3-6. This is *another* combination *motor and generator*. The motor
operates on ac, and the generator provides a dc output. The *rotary
converter* changes ___ to _____ .
*

— — — — — — — — — — — — — —

ac

dc

3-7. The rotary converter is a dc _____ turned by an ac
_____ .
*

— — — — — — — — — — — — — —

generator

motor

The Inverter

3-8. The *inverter* is a rotary converter in reverse. It is a combination dc motor and ac generator. This device changes the _____
input to an _____ output.
*

dc
ac

3-9. The inverter is an ac _____ turned by a dc _____.
*

generator
motor

The Vibrator

3-10. The *vibrator* comes in *two* types and each type has a particular function. One type *changes* dc to ac; the other type *increases* the amplitude of the dc input. This drawing illustrates the functional parts of a vibrator.

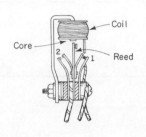

The input voltage causes current through contacts 1 to *energize* the coil. This moves the *reed*, opening contacts 1 and closing contacts 2. With contacts 1 open, coil current is *interrupted*. The coil *denergizes* and allows the reed to swing back to its original position. This *opens* contacts 2, and closes contacts 1. When contacts 1 close, *another cycle* of operation is started. This operation is the same for both types. The vibrator is designed to either change _____ to _____ or increase the amplitude of the input _____.

*

— — — — — — — — — — — — — — — —

dc
ac
dc

3-11. When contacts 1 close, the coil _____ . This _____ contacts 2 and _____ contacts 1.

*

— — — — — — — — — — — — — — — —

energizes
closes
opens

3-12. Opening contacts 1 causes the coil to _____ and allows the reed to _____ contacts 2 and _____ contacts 1.

*

— — — — — — — — — — — — — — — — —

deenergize
open
close

3-13. The *output coil* is not shown in frame 3-10. This coil is energized through both sets of contacts. If the vibrator is designed for a *dc output*, both contacts energize it in the same direction. If it is designed for an *ac output*, contacts 1 and 2 energize the coil in *opposite* directions. The output coil is energized through both sets of _____ .

*

— — — — — — — — — — — — — — — — —

contacts

3-14. If both contacts energize the output coil in the *same direction*, the output is _____ . This output will be of a _____ amplitude than the input.

*

— — — — — — — — — — — — — — — — —

dc
greater

3-15. If the contacts energize the output coil in *opposite directions*, the output is _____ . This type of vibrator changes the _____ input to an _____ output.
*

___ ___ ___ ___ ___ ___ ___ ___ ___ ___ ___ ___

ac
dc
ac

Multiphase Generator

3-16. The *single phase* ac generator uses *one set* of slip rings and provides a *single* sine wave of output voltage. *Two and three phase* generators are also used. Generators are designed to provide one, two, or three _____ outputs.
*

___ ___ ___ ___ ___ ___ ___ ___ ___ ___ ___ ___

phase

3-17. This drawing illustrates a *two phase* generator with its *two* output sine waves.

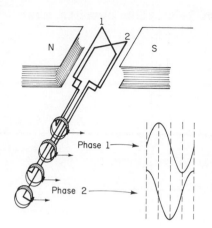

Phase 1 →

Phase 2 →

Each loop represents armature windings. *Each phase* has its own armature winding and output slip rings. The effect is the same as *two generators* on the same shaft. Winding 1 generates the phase 1 voltage, and the phase 2 voltage is generated by winding 2. A two phase generator is equivalent to _____ generators on a _____ shaft.

*

two
single

3-18. In the drawing of frame 3-17, *each phase* has its own armature _____ and output _____ _____ .

*

winding
slip rings

3-19. The number of slip rings can be *reduced* by having *one common* ring and *one additional* ring for each phase. It is not necessary to have a _____ of rings for each phase. One _____ ring will serve all phases.

*

pair
common

103

3-20.   If the outputs are *balanced*, there is *no current* in the *common* lead.   In this case, the common lead and ring can be *eliminated*.   In order to dispense with the common lead, the outputs must be perfectly _____ .

*

— — — — — — — — — — — — — — — — — — — —

balanced

3-21.   In frame 3–17, the windings are physically *separated* by 90°. This means that the two outputs are 90° out of _____ .

*

— — — — — — — — — — — — — — — — — — — —

phase

3-22.   The windings of a three phase generator are schematically represented as either Y or Δ.

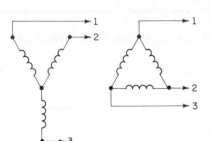

Both types provide *three* different outputs.   The windings are physically *separated* by 120° and each output is _____ degrees out of phase with the other two.

*

— — — — — — — — — — — — — — — — — — — —

120

3-23. The three phase generator *seldom* uses a common lead. An output is taken between *any two* adjacent leads. Thus, each output is 1.73 times the voltage on a single winding. If each winding develops 100 volts, each output will be _____.

*

— — — — — — — — — — — — — — — —

1.73 x 100 = 173 volts

3-24. This drawing illustrates the *phase relation* of the three outputs.

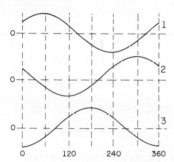

Each output is 120° out of phase with _____ of the others. Phase 2 _____ phase 1 by 120° and _____ phase 3 by 120°.

*

— — — — — — — — — — — — — — — —

both

leads

lags

3-25. More than 90% of the power used in the United States comes from an *ac source*. For most of us, ac is as near as the nearest wall plug. Yet, *very little* electronic equipment can use ac. Most power is funished from ____ sources, but it is not in a usable form for _____ equipment.

*

— — — — — — — — — — — — — — — —

ac

most

3-26. If you trace the power cord into a piece of electronic
equipment, the *first component* you encounter is a *transformer*. The
primary *purpose* of the power transformer is to change the *amplitude*
of ac. The power _____ is used in nearly all electronic
equipment to change the _____ of ac.
*

———

transformer
amplitude

3-27. The transformer is composed of a *primary winding* for the
input and a *secondary winding* for the output. This is the *minimum*
configuration. Some have *more than one* primary and *several* secondaries. The only connection between primary and secondary is a
magnetic field. The minimum configuration for a transformer is one
_____ and one _____ . The windings are connected by a
_____ field.
*

———

primary
secondary
magnetic

3-28.   The input ac causes a *changing flux* in the primary which *cuts across* the windings of the secondary.   This induces an ac into the secondary.   In effect the input is coupled through a _____ field to the output.   The input is ac and the output is _____ .
*

— — — — — — — — — — — — — —

magnetic
ac

Construction of Transformers

3-29.   Power transformers are constructed with *iron alloy cores* to increase the *coupling efficiency*.   Induced currents circulate in these cores and cause *losses*.   The currents are called *eddy currents* and the losses are *eddy current losses*.   The iron core increases _____ efficiency but causes losses due to _____ _____ in the core.
*

— — — — — — — — — — — — — —

coupling
eddy currents

3-30. Eddy current losses can be greatly reduced by *laminating* the core.

E + I combination   O rings

Each lamination is covered with an *insulating varnish*. This shortens the path for the eddy currents. E and I combination and O rings are two of the popular lamination *patterns*. A laminated core decreases eddy current _____ by _____ the path for eddy currents.

*
— — — — — — — — — — — — —

losses

shortening

3-31. The E and I combination has *fewer* losses and makes a more *compact* transformer than the O rings.

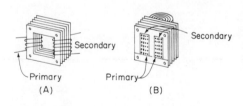

Secondary   Secondary

Primary   Primary
(A)   (B)

Notice in drawing B that the secondary is wound directly *over* the primary and both coils are *inside* the core. Placing primary and secondary so close together decreases the _____ . Placing both coils within the core reduces the physical _____ of the transformer.

*
— — — — — — — — — — — — —

losses

size

3-32. Transformers may have *several* secondary windings. A separate output is provided by *each* secondary. All outputs have the *same* *frequency* as the input, *but* both phase and amplitude may be different. All windings of a transformer have a common _____.
*

——— ——— ——— ——— ——— ——— ——— ——— ——— ——— ——— ———

frequency

3-33. The voltage amplitude *relation* between input and output depends upon the *turns ratio* of primary to secondary. When the primary has *more turns* than the secondary, the output voltage is *less* than the input. When the primary has *fewer turns* than the secondary, the output voltage is *more than* the input. A transformer may increase or decrease the ac input depending upon the _____ _____ between primary and secondary.
*

—— —— —— —— —— —— —— —— —— —— —— ——

turns ratio

3-34. When the voltage output is *larger* than the input, the transformer is a *step-up* transformer. The step-up transformer has more turns on the _____ than it has on the _____ .
*

—— —— —— —— —— —— —— —— —— —— —— ——

secondary
primary

3-35. The output voltage from a *step-down* transformer is *smaller* than the input. The step-down transformer has more turns on the _____ than it has on the _____ .

*

— — — — — — — — — — — — —

primary

secondary

3-36. The *phase relation* between input voltage is either in phase or *180° out of phase*. This is determined by the *direction* of the windings on primary and secondary. A transformer may be wound to produce either _____ phase shift or _____ degree phase shift.

*

— — — — — — — — — — — — — —

zero

180

3-37. This drawing shows schematic symbols for *iron core* transformers. Unless otherwise specified, the coil on the *left* is the primary. Transformer A has one primary while B has _____ primaries.

*

— — — — — — — — — — — — —

two

3-38. Transformer A in frame 3-37 has *one* output. Transformer B
has _____ secondaries and _____ outputs.
*

— — — — — — — — — — — — — — —

three
three

3-39. The two *dots* on transformer A in frame 3-37 indicate points
of like *phase*. The input (1 to 2) is ___ _____ with the output
(3 to 4).
*

— — — — — — — — — — — — — — —

in phase

3-40. The dots may or *may not* appear on a schematic. Without the
dots, the phase relation of primary to secondary is not readily
discernable. Whether or not dots are used, the secondary voltage
is either in phase or _____ degrees out of phase with the primary.
The phase is dependent upon the _____ of the windings.
*

— — — — — — — — — — — — — — —

180
direction

3-41. Apart from transformer losses which *reduce* the output, the output voltage is controlled by *two factors*. These are primary to secondary *turns ratio* and the *amplitude of the input* voltage. Let's assume that we have an *ideal* transformer and remove the losses from our discussion for a while. We can then express the remaining factors in an *inverse ratio*: turns in the primary x voltage of the secondary = turns in the secondary x voltage of the primary. A transformer with 10 turns on the primary and 40 turns on the secondary has a 100 volt input. What is the output voltage?
*

— — — — — — — — — — — —

$10X = 40 \times 100$. Output = 400 volts.

3-42. *Normally* primary and secondary are *designated* as P and S respectively, and they appear as *subscripts* to values. N indicates number of turns. The transformer ratios in frame 3-41 can be written thus: $N_p E_s = N_s E_p$. This ratio states that the _____ of the primary times the voltage of the secondary is equal to the _____ of the secondary times the voltage of the primary.
*

— — — — — — — — — — — —

turns

turns

3-43. This drawing illustrates a method of *designating* the turns
ratio. A is a *step-up* transformer and B is a *step-down* transformer.

(A)   (B)

The numbers are not normally the actual
turns *count* as it appears here; they express
a ratio. In transformer A, there are 6
turns on the secondary for each ____ turns
on the primary. In transformer B, the ratio
is reversed; there are 4 turns on the secondary for each ____ turns on the primary.

*

4

8

3-44. These ratios are generally expressed as the *lowest whole
numbers*. In this case, A in frame 4-43 is a ____ to ____ step-up
transformer, and B is a 2 to 1 _____ transformer.

*

2

3

step-down

3-45. If we *compare* the turns ratio to the voltage ratio, we have
$E_p/E_s = N_p/N_s$. This simply says that the voltage ratio is directly
proportional to the _____ _____.

*

turns ratio

3-46. The laws of nature don't permit us to get something for nothing. So, when voltage is stepped up or down, the current is changed in the *opposite direction* by the same ratio. When we compare current ratio to turns ratio, we have $I_s/I_p = N_p/N_s$. This says that the current ratio is _____ proportional to the turns ratio.

*

— — — — — — — — — — — — — — — — — — — —

inversely

3-47. A 1 to 2 *step-up* transformer will _____ the voltage and reduce the current by _____ percent.

*

— — — — — — — — — — — — — — — — — — — —

double
50

Impedance

3-48. Impedance couples *both ways* through a transformer. Therefore, the *impedance ratio* is directly proportional to the *square* of the turns ratio: $Z_p/Z_s = (N_p/N_s)^2$. When the turns ratio is doubled, the impedance ratio is increased to _____ times its original value.

*

— — — — — — — — — — — — — — — — — — — —

four

3-49. Since transformers can be purchased with a *great variety* of turns ratios, they are a favorite device for *matching impedance* between two circuits. For *maximum* power transfer through any coupling, the two impedances must be the same. Suppose that one circuit has an output impedance of 1250 ohms, and you need to couple it into a cable with an impedance of 50 ohms. A direct coupling would cause a large power loss, but a 5 to 1 step-down transformer can fill the gap. This transformer can *match* the 1250 ohm output and the 50 ohm input and accomplish maximum power transfer.

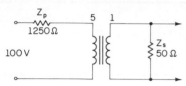

The 1250 ohm Z_p matches the high _____ impedance of the previous stage. The 50 ohm Z_s matches the low _____ impedance of the cable.

*

— — — — — — — — — — — —

output

input

3-50. In frame 3-49, the 100 volts E_p will produce only 20 volts in the secondary, but current (I_s) will be *5 times* I_p. Therefore, the power in the primary is the same as the power in the _____ .
*

— — — — — — — — — — — —

secondary

3-51. I_p = 100V/1250Ω = _____ .
*

0.08 ampere

3-52. $I_s = 5 \times 0.08 =$ _____ .

*

— — — — — — — — — — — — — — — — — —

0.4 ampere

3-53. $P_p = 100V\ (0.08A) =$ _____ .

*

— — — — — — — — — — — — — — — — — —

8 watts

3-54. $P_s = 20V\ (0.4A) =$ _____ .

*

— — — — — — — — — — — — — — — — — —

8 watts

3-55. These simple calculations show that impedance has been
_____ and _____ power transfer has been accomplished.

*

— — — — — — — — — — — — — — — — — —

matched
maximum

116

3-56. The *only perfect* transformers exist in text books. A real transformer has *three kinds of losses: copper* loss, *hysteresis* loss, and *eddy current* loss. The copper loss is due to the *dc resistance* of the primary and secondary windings. This resistance dissipates energy in the form of heat which constitutes _____ _____ .
*

— — — — — — — — — — — — — —

power loss

3-57. The *hysteresis loss* is caused by *residual magnetism* in the iron core. Each time voltage passes through zero, a *coercive force* is required to cancel the residual magnetism. This force requires energy which is a _____ _____ .
*

— — — — — — — — — — — — — —

power loss

3-58. *Eddy current losses* are caused by *induced currents* circulating through the *iron core*. These currents set up flux in the core and cause loss from *heat*. The flux also does some *shielding* of the winding causing further loss. Eddy current losses are caused from _____ currents circulating in the _____ _____ .
*

— — — — — — — — — — — — — —

induced
iron core

3-59. *Laminating* the core reduces eddy currents, but they are still there. The eddy current losses are directly proportional to the square of the *lamination thickness*. Eddy current losses are always present in an _____ core transformer. These losses can be reduced by _____ the core.

*

— — — — — — — — — — — — — —

iron
laminating

Efficiency

3-60. Transformer *efficiency* is a ratio of power out to power in: Eff. = P_{in}/P_{out}. In our perfect transformer, efficiency was always unity. In practice, the unity figure can be approached but *never* quite attained. P_{in}/P_{out} is _____.

*

— — — — — — — — — — — — — —

efficiency

3-61. The practical transformer always has an efficiency less than _____ .

*

— — — — — — — — — — — — — —

unity

3-62. Efficiency can also be expressed as a percentage:

   % Eff. = $(P_{in}/P_{out})(100)$

An efficiency of 0.99 is equivalent to a percent of efficiency of

_____ percent.

*

0.99 x 100 = 99

3-63. In frame 3-62, the remaining 1% represents energy used by
copper, hysteresis, and eddy current _____ .

*

---

losses

CLASSIFICATION OF TRANSFORMERS

3-64. Transformers are *classed* according to the range of *frequencies*
they can handle. In electronics we are concerned with *three* classes:
power frequency, *audio* frequency, and *radio* frequency. The radio
frequency transformers come in two types, *tuned and untuned*. The
three classes of transformers concerning electronics are power frequency, _____ _____ , and _____ _____ .

*

---

audio frequency
radio frequency

3-65. The radio frequency class has transformers that are _____ and others that are _____ .

*

— — — — — — — — — — —

tuned
untuned

Power Frequency

3-66. A *power* frequency transformer is designed to handle *one* specific frequency in the *range* from 60 Hz to 1600 Hz. Power frequencies range from 60 to _____ Hz and a power transformer can handle _____ of these frequencies.

*

— — — — — — — — — — —

1600
one

3-67. *Stationary and home* entertainment equipment use either 110V or 220V, 60 Hz transformers. These will be one, two, or three phase to suit the need. *Mobile and airborne* equipment generally use either 400 Hz or 1600 Hz transformers which may also be either single or multiple phase. The *higher frequencies* enable the construction of more *compact* power supplies. Low power frequencies are used in _____ or home _____ equipment.

*

— — — — — — — — — — —

stationary
entertainment

3-68. The higher frequencies enable use of more _____ power
supplies and are used in mobile and _____ equipment.
*

— — — — — — — — — — — — — — — — — — — —

compact
airborne

Audio Frequencies

3-69. The *audio frequency* band overlaps the power band. It starts
at about 16 Hz and goes up to about 20 kHz. This should be all frequencies detectable by the *human ear*. All _____ frequencies
fall into the audio _____ which ranges from about ____ Hz to
about 20 kHz.
*

— — — — — — — — — — — — — — — — — — — —

audible
band
16

3-70. Frequencies from 100 Hz to 4000 Hz are generally referred to
as the *mid-frequencies* of the audio band. Probably the reason for
this is the fact that nearly *everyone* can hear this range of frequencies. The mid-audio frequencies are _____ to most people.
*

— — — — — — — — — — — — — — — — — — — —

audible

3-71. A good audio transformer will amplify the *mid-frequencies* with very little distortion. The band pass of a good audio amplifier includes frequencies from _____ to _____ Hz.
*

— — — — — — — — — — — — — — — —

100
4000

3-72. An audio transformer resembles the power transformer in many ways, but the core material is *more critical, efficiency* is higher, and *stray capacitance* is reduced to a minimum. Efficiency may be as high as 0.999. The audio transformer is more critical than the _____ transformer, and it operates at a higher _____ .
*

— — — — — — — — — — — — — — — —

power
efficiency

3-73. The audio transformer is used to drive *speakers* in public address systems, broadcast equipment, and communications receivers. One wide use of the audio transformer is to drive _____ .
*

— — — — — — — — — — — — — — — —

speakers

3-74. This is a *broad* band. It starts at about 16 kHz and goes up to the lower *light* frequencies; about 10 THz (T=10^{12}). The radio frequency band ranges from _____ frequencies to _____ frequencies.

*

— — — — — — — — — — — — — —

audio
light

3-75. In the *low* frequencies, the radio transformer uses an *iron core*. This gives way to *powdered* iron and to the *air* core as the frequency gets *higher*. This is a schematic symbol for an air core transformer.

The core material changes from _____ to powdered iron, to _____ as the frequency increases.

*

— — — — — — — — — — — — — —

iron
air

123

3-76. *Fewer turns* of wire are required for windings at the higher frequencies. There comes a point when *two straight wires* constitute the primary and secondary of a transformer. On up the band, the transformer is *abandoned* in favor of other types of coupling. As frequency goes up, the number of turns _____ . Finally the transformer is _____ for other types of coupling.
*

---

decreases
abandoned

Tuned Radio Frequency

3-77. The *tuned* transformer *is not* limited to radio frequencies, but it is *used more* in this area. Most radio frequency transformers pass a *wide band* of frequencies. The tuned transformer is designed to pass a *very narrow band*. When a narrow band transformer is needed, a _____ transformer is used.
*

---

tuned

3-78. Designing a tuned transformer is a simple matter. *Adding a capacitor* across either or both primary and secondary will change a common transformer into a tuned transformer. The size of the capacitor is selected to form a *resonant* tank with the inductance of the winding. This is a *parallel tuned circuit* for the one resonant frequency. A capacitor across a winding forms a _____ circuit for the _____ frequency.
*

— — — — — — — — — — — — — — — — —

tuned
resonant

3-79. The circuit will *pass* the resonant frequency with a high level of efficiency but will *discriminate* against all other frequencies. Only a narrow band of frequencies around the _____ frequency is passed by the tuned transformer.
*

— — — — — — — — — — — — — — — — —

resonant

RECTIFICATION

3-80. *Rectification* is the process of changing ac to a _____ dc.
*

— — — — — — — — — — — — — — — — —

pulsating

3-81. The device for rectification is called a *rectifier* and it is
generally some form of *diode*. Rectification is performed by
_____ , and when so used, they are called _____ .
*

— — — — — — — — — — — — — — — —

diodes
rectifiers

Half-Wave Rectifier

3-82. A rectifier circuit is named according to the way it performs.
A *half-wave* rectifier passes *one alternation* of the input and eliminates the other. A half-wave rectifier passes only _____ of the
input ac.
*

— — — — — — — — — — — — — — — —

half

3-83. The portion of the ac that is passed is dc, but it has many
peaks and valleys. This is a typical half-wave rectifier circuit.

This diode will conduct each time
point C becomes _____ . The
output at point E will be a series of
_____ pulses.

*

— — — — — — — — — — — — — — — —

positive
positive

3-84. This is a time amplitude *graph* of the signals in the circuit of frame 3-83.

From T_1 to T_2 the diode is _____ _____ and the output is _____ .

Primary
1

Secondary
2

Output
3

*
cut off
zero

3-85. From T_2 to T_3 the diode is _____ and the output follows the _____ .

*
conducting
input

3-86. The diode is cut off again from _____ to _____ and conducts again from _____ to _____ .

*
T_3
T_4
T_4
T_5

3-87. The *average* value of the output from a half-wave rectifier is $(0.637/2)(E_{peak})$. For a 100 volt peak to peak on the secondary, the average output is _____ volts.

*

— — — — — — — — — — — — — — —

$0.3185 \times 50 = 15.9$

3-88. The output from a half-wave rectifier would produce a very *erratic current*. It is also *difficult* to smooth out all the hills and valleys, *but* it is widely used in circuits which require a high voltage with very little current. *Many* electronic circuits require high voltage but use little or no current. The _____ wave rectifier is well suited for supplying _____ to these circuits.

*

— — — — — — — — — — — — — — —

half-

voltage

3-89. Diodes may be connected in *parallel* as shown here.

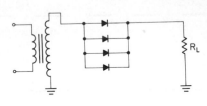

These diodes will conduct and cut off in *unison* which enables the circuit to handle more current. Current capacity is _____ by adding diodes in

_____ .

*

— — — — — — — — — — — — — — —

increased

parallel

3-90. The output of the circuit in frame 3-89 is still a _____ wave output, but the total current is _____ among the diodes.
*

— — — — — — — — — — — — — — — —

half-
divided

3-91. Rectifiers discussed thus far have been *positive* rectifiers; that is, they *pass the positive* alternation and *eliminate the negative* alternation. They can be changed to negative rectifiers by *reversing* the diodes in the circuit. The negative rectifier will pass the _____ alternation and eliminate the _____ alternation.
*

— — — — — — — — — — — — — — — —

negative
positive

3-92. The *full-wave* rectifier has *at least one* diode to conduct on *each* alternation. A typical circuit is shown here.

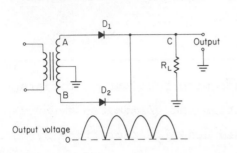

Output voltage

D_1 conducts when point A is positive, and D_2 conducts when point B is positive. The current for both diodes is from ground through R_L. When D_1 conducts, D_2 is cut off, and a _____ _____ is developed across R_L. A similar output is developed when D_1 is _____ _____ and D_2 _____.

*

_____

positive pulse

cut off

conducts

_____

3-93. Since the secondary of this transformer is *grounded, only one-half* of the delivered peak voltage is applied to each diode. For a given transformer, the maximum output of a full-wave rectifier is only _____ the maximum output of a half-wave rectifier.

*

_____

half

3-94. Since the peaks are *closer together* and the valleys are *less pronounced*, the full-wave output is fairly easy to change to a smooth dc. It can furnish *heavy* currents, but the output voltage is somewhat *limited*. This type of rectifier supplies voltage to circuits which require _____ current and relatively _____ voltage.
*

high
low

3-95. The full-wave rectifier may also use several diodes in *parallel* as shown here.

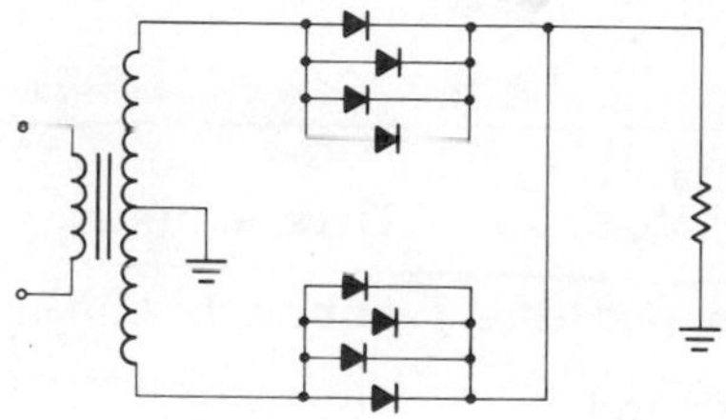

Multiple diodes will not alter the wave shape, but this arrangement permits more _____ without danger of overloading a single diode.

*

current

3-96. *Most* rectifiers do use multiple diodes. So, for sake of simplicity, we will revert to a single diode representation. Most rectifiers use _____ diodes to increase the _____ capacity of the circuit.
*

multiple
current

3-97. The bridge rectifier is a full-wave rectifier, but it delivers a higher voltage output than the previous circuit.

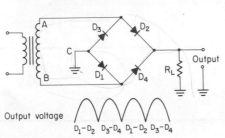

Output voltage

D_1-D_2 D_3-D_4 D_1-D_2 D_3-D_4

Two diodes conduct on *each* alternation of the input. This enables an output equivalent to the full *peak* voltage of the input. The output is similar to that of a full-wave rectifier with amplitude the same as a _____ rectifier.

*

- - - - - - - - - - - - -

half-wave

3-98. When point A is *positive*, point B is *negative*. This causes current from ground through R_L, through D_2 to point A, through the winding to point B, and through D_1 back to ground. The output is equivalent to the _____ amplitude between points A and B.

*

- - - - - - - - - - - - -

peak

3-99. On the next alternation, point B is *positive* and point A is *negative*. This causes current from ground through R_L, through D_4 to point B, through the winding to point A, and through D_3 back to ground. This also develops a _____ pulse equal to the peak amplitude between point B and point A.

*

- - - - - - - - - - - - -

positive

3-100. This rectifier can provide relatively *high current and voltage* while retaining the advantage of being *easy* to smooth out. The bridge rectifier has the advantages of both the _____ wave and the _____ wave rectifiers.
*

half-
full-

3-101. The bridge rectifier in frame 3-97 is a *positive* rectifier. It can be changed to a negative rectifier by *reversing* all four diodes in the circuit. Any positive rectifier can be changed to a negative rectifier by _____ all diodes.
*

reversing

THREE PHASE POWER

3-102. Three phase power *requires* three phase generators, three phase _____ , and three phase _____ .
*

transformers
rectifiers

3-103. This is a Δ to Y, *three phase* transformer.

The delta section is the _____ and
the Y section is the _____ .

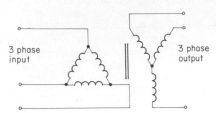

3 phase
input

3 phase
output

*
— — — — — — —

primary

secondary

3-104. Any rectifier discussed thus far is *suitable* for use with
the three phase transformer. This is the *half-wave* rectifier
arrangement.

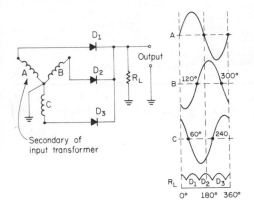

Secondary of
input transformer

Sine waves A, B, and C are developed
on coils A, B, and C, respectively.
Each diode conducts for 120° during
the *most positive* portion of its input.
This keeps current through R_L all the
time. The output remains at a *high*
level, and the ripple is *relatively*
small. There is a slight peak in the
output for each _____ peak of
each _____ _____ .

*
— — — — — — — — —

positive

sine wave

SUMMARY

1. The two most common sources of voltage are *batteries* and *generators*.

2. Power *conversion units* are used in *nearly all* power systems.

3. A *dynamotor* changes the input dc to either a higher or lower output dc.

4. The dynamotor is a *dc motor* turning a *dc generator*.

5. The *rotary converter* changes ac to dc.

6. The *inverter* changes dc to ac.

7. *Vibrators* are of two types. One changes dc to ac; the other increases the amplitude of dc.

8. The *three phase generator* supplies three outputs which are 120° out of phase with adjacent outputs.

9. The *two phase generator* furnishes two outputs which are 180° out of phase.

10. The *transformer* is a device which adjusts an input ac to a usable level.

11. *Core laminations* reduce losses in a transformer by limiting eddy currents.

12. The *direction of the windings* determine phase relation between primary and secondary of a transformer.

13. A *step-up* transformer has the greatest number of turns on its secondary.

14. The output *voltage is directly* proportional to the *turns ratio*. The output current is inversely proportional to the turns ratio.

15. *Maximum power* is transferred when output impedance *matches* input impedance. The *transformer* can be used to match widely different impedances.

16. Transformers suffer from *three types* of losses: *copper*, *hysteresis*, and *eddy current*.

17. Transformers are *classed* according to the frequency they handle.

18. *Power transformers* generally are designed for one of three frequencies: 60 Hz, 400 Hz, or 1600 Hz.

19. A *tuned transformer* passes a very narrow band of frequencies.

20. *Rectification* changes ac to pulsating dc.

21. A *half-wave* rectifier furnishes one pulse of dc for each sine wave of input ac.

22. Half-wave rectifiers are used in circuits which need a *high voltage and a low current*.

23. Most rectifiers use *multiple diodes* in parallel to increase the current capacity.

24. The full-wave rectifier produces *a pulse* out for *each alternation* of the input sine wave.

25. The full-wave rectifier supplies voltages to circuits requiring relatively *low voltage and high current*.

26. The *bridge rectifier* has the advantages of both the half- and full-wave rectifiers.

27. *Three phase generators* are matched with three phase transformers and three phase rectifiers.

SECTION 4
VOLTAGE CONTROL

Proper *voltage control* is the key to properly operating equipment. Practically all equipment malfunctions are either *caused by* an improper voltage condition or else the malfunction *will cause* an improper voltage condition. Regardless of which caused the other, voltage control is the key. So far, ac has been delivered, altered to a usable level, and rectified to a pulsating dc. It is still *unfit* for most applications. Now we need to remove the ac ripple, shape the voltage to our exact needs, and establish automatic controls.

VOLTAGE MULTIPLIER

4-1. Rectifiers generally furnish voltages at some intermediate amplitude which is *reasonably close* to most circuit requirements. For *extra large* voltage requirements, this voltage amplitude must be *increased*. The same voltage must have the amplitude *decreased* to satisfy the *low voltage* requirements. Apart from the conversion units previously discussed, *electronic circuits* can be used to *alter* voltage amplitude. The amplitude of dc voltage must be _____ to fit either very high or very low voltage requirements. This can be done with either _____ units or _____ circuits.
*
— — — — — — — — — — — — — — —

altered
conversion
electronic

4-2. The *voltage multiplier* is an electronic circuit which increases the amplitude of a dc voltage. When high voltages are required, a _____ _____ may be used to _____ the rectifier output.
*
— — — — — — — — — — — — — — —

voltage multiplier
increase

4-3. There are several varieties of voltage multipliers. They can be designed to *double*, *triple*, or *quadruple* the input voltage. This is a voltage doubler.

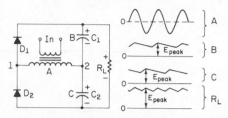

A dc voltage can be raised to nearly any desired level by using one or more _____ _____ stages. A circuit can be designed to _____ the input by a factor of 2, 3, or 4.

*

— — — — — — — — — — — —

voltage multiplier

multiply

— — — — — — — — — — — —

4-4. In frame 4-3, point 1 is *positive* and point 2 is *negative* for *one alternation*. During this time, current is from point 2 through C_1 and through D_1 to point 1. This charges C_1 to the peak value of the input, wave shape A. During one alternation, D_1 conducts and charges _____ to the _____ value of the input.

*

— — — — — — — — — — — —

C_1

peak

4-5. On the *next alternation*, point 2 is *positive* and point 1 is *negative*. Current is now from point 1 through D_2 and through C_2 to point 2. When ____ conducts, it charges ____ to the _____ value of the input.

*

— — — — — — — — — — — — — —

D_2
C_2
peak

___

4-6. The charges on the capacitors are in *series* and the *only* discharge path is through R_L. The full value of the combined *charge* is impressed across R_L. The voltage across R_L is equivalent to _____ the _____ value of the input voltage.

*

— — — — — — — — — — — — — —

twice
peak

___

4-7. R_L is a very *large* resistor, and voltage multipliers are used in areas where *very little* current is needed. This gives the capacitors very little opportunity to discharge. After the first full sine wave input, the diodes conduct *very briefly* at the signal peaks; just enough to *replenish* the charge on the capacitors. The output across R_L is very nearly a steady ____ with an amplitude _____ as large as the peak input.

*

— — — — — — — — — — — — — —

dc
twice

4-8. Voltage doublers are frequently required to furnish voltages *in excess* of 10 kV. In this case, *single capacitors* capable of this kind of charge are pretty bulky and very expensive. The problem is solved like this.

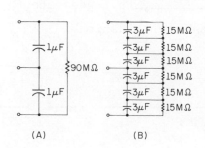

(A)   (B)

Circuits A and B are *equivalent* to each other with the same total capacitance and resistance. The output is the same for both circuits, but in circuit B, total voltage is _____ among several capacitors.

*

— — — — — — — — — — — — —

distributed (divided)

4-9. In frame 4-8, the resistor is divided and shorting bars inserted to *equalize* distribution of charge among the capacitors. With an input peak of 3000 volts, each capacitor in circuit A is charged to _____ volts while each capacitor in circuit B is charged to _____ volts.

*

— — — — — — — — — — — — —

3000
1000

4-10. Another arrangement of the components in frame 4-3 will produce this circuit.

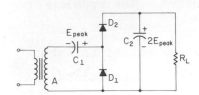

This is a *cascade* voltage doubler. This
circuit performs the same task as the previous _____ _____ but goes about
it in a slightly different fashion.

*

___ ___ ___ ___ ___ ___ ___ ___ ___ ___ ___ ___

voltage doubler

4-11. In frame 4-10, when point A goes *positive*, D_1 conducts and
charges C_1 to the *peak* input in the direction indicated. On the
next alternation, point A is *negative*, and the input is in *series*
with the charge on C_1. This places a _____ potential equivalent to *twice* the peak input on the collector of ___.
*

___ ___ ___ ___ ___ ___ ___ ___ ___ ___ ___ ___

positive

D_2

4-12. Under the conditions described in frame 4-11, *current is* from
point A, through C_2, through D_2, and into C_1. C_2 charges to *twice*
the input *peak* value in the direction indicated. The charge on C_2
is impressed across R_L and constitutes the output voltage. When the
secondary of this transformer has a 3000 volt peak, C_2 is charged to
_____ volts and the output is _____ volts.
*

___ ___ ___ ___ ___ ___ ___ ___ ___ ___ ___ ___

6000
6000

4-13. The cascade doubler may have sections added to increase its multiplication factor. Adding one section changes it to this *tripler*.

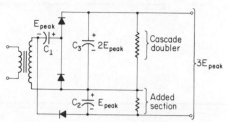

The output of this circuit is _____ times as large as the _____ input.

*

- - - - - - - - - - - - - - - - -

three

peak

4-14. In frame 4-13, when the input is 3000 volts peak, C_1 and C_2 *each* charge to _____ volts and C_3 charges to _____ volts.
*

- - - - - - - - - - - - - - - - -

3000

6000

4-15. Adding another section to the tripler produces this *voltage quadrupler*.

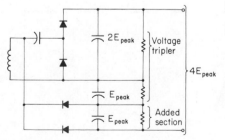

Now for *every volt* of peak ac input the output is _____ volts of dc.

*

- - - - - - - - - - - - - - - - -

four

4-16. Conceivably many more sections *could be* added and each section would increase the multiplication factor by _____.

*
_____

one

FILTERING

4-17. *Filtering* is the process of reducing the ac *ripple* of a pulsating dc. This ripple is present to some extent in the output of all rectifiers. Without filtering, this voltage is *unsatisfactory* for most circuits. A pulsating dc contains an ac _____ which must be _____ by _____ .

*
_____

ripple
reduced
filtering

4-18. The *ideal*, perfectly smooth dc is *seldom* attained, but a filter will remove part of the _____ and change the rectifier output to a usable dc.

*
_____

ripple

4-19.   Several previous circuits have used capacitor input filters. This is the *simplest* version of a filter and consists of a *capacitor in parallel with a resistor*.   Here it is shown filtering the output of a half-wave rectifier.

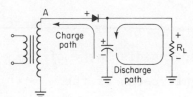

This is also called an RC filter because the load resistor performs part of the _____ action.

*

filtering

4-20.   When point A (frame 4-19) goes *positive*, the diode conducts and develops a *positive pulse* across R_L while charging the capacitor as indicated.   During the next alternation the diode is _____ _____ and the capacitor is _____ through R_L.
*

cut off

discharging

4-21.   The amount of discharge permitted between positive inputs is determined by the *time constant* (R x C) and the frequency of the input.   There will be some positive voltage across R_L until the capacitor is completely _____.
*

discharged

4-22. When the filter has a *long* time constant for the input frequency, the capacitor will never completely discharge. The capacitor discharge then partially fills in the valleys between the positive

_____ .

*

— — — — — — — — — — — — —

peaks

4-23. When loads are added that *draw current*, the discharge of the capacitor is *hastened*. This *reduces* the effectiveness of the

_____ action.

*

— — — — — — — — — — — — —

filtering

4-24. The RC, capacitor input filter is good for circuits which require a *high voltage* with a _____ current.

*

— — — — — — — — — — — — —

4-25. Adding an *inductor* to the filter produces an LC filter but it may still be a capacitor input.

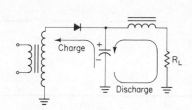

This is a L type, capacitor input, LC filter. This is a much *better* filter because the inductor offers practically no opposition to dc but strongly opposes the ac components. The capacitor charges *quickly* through the _____ but discharges *slowly* through the resistor and _____.

*

diode

inductor

4-26. The inductor uses an *iron core* and is called a *choke* coil because of its ability to suppress the ___ components.

*

ac

4-27. The *field* of the coil combines with the *charge* on the capacitor to keep a near *constant* current in the *same direction* through R_L. The capacitor discharges very little, and most of the _____ is removed from the output.

*

ripple

4-28.   The current through R_L *never* changes _____ and has
only small *variations* in its _____ .
*

---

direction
amplitude

4-29.   Here is another version of the capacitor input filter.

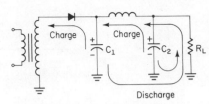

This is a pi (π) type, capacitor input,
LC filter. Adding a second capacitor to
the circuit enables *more* output current
without greatly *reducing* the effectiveness
of the _____ .

*

---

filter

4-30.   On the *charging* action, C_1 is fully charged before the charge
on C_2 is started. During *discharge*, C_2 is fully discharged before
C_1 starts to lose its charge. Combining this with the action of the
coil makes a very effective filter. Sudden changes will be *blocked*
by the choke and *shorted* out by the _____ . The slower
ripple is smoothed out by the discharge of the _____ components.
*

---

capacitors
reactive

4-31. When voltage is furnished to loads which *draw appreciable current*, the full-wave rectifier is used. The *capacitor input* filters are very effective when combined with the *full-wave rectifier*. The capacitors in the filter will charge _____ as often which means the discharge cycle is only _____ as long.

*

— — — — — — — — — — — — — — — —

twice

half

Choke Input Filters

4-32. When *currents are high* enough to reduce the effectiveness of the capacitor input filter, we resort to a *choke input* filter. This is a L type filter with an inductor in series with total current.

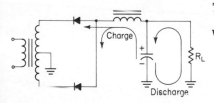

This is a choke input, LC _____ used with a _____ wave rectifier.

*

— — — — — — — — — — — — — — — —

filter

full-

149

4-33. On *each alternation*, one of the diodes will *conduct* and charge the reactive components. The cut off time is *very short* and little discharge is permitted. Even with relatively high current, the output is a smooth _____ with an amplitude equivalent to _____ the peak voltage of the transformer secondary.

*
— — — — — — — — — — — — —

dc

half

4-34. This is an *improved* filter.

It is simply two L type, _____ input filters.

Input from rectifier   Filtered output

*
— — — — — — — — — — — — —

choke

4-35. This filter stands up well under *both* high current and changing current. Now we have two _____ in series with total circuit current.

*
— — — — — — — — — — — — —

inductors (chokes)

4-36. The load resistor is frequently physically *removed* from the filter circuit. To *make sure* that the reactive components always have a *discharge path*, a *bleeder resistor* is normally inserted. The bleeder is *parallel* to the load when the load is connected. But when the load is removed, the bleeder is still there.

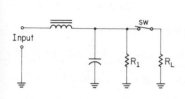

A good filter will hold a charge for *days* if it has no discharge path. The bleeder resistor provides a high resistance path and allows the charge to gradually *bleed away* when power and load are removed. The primary purpose of the bleeder is _____ . It decreases the probability of a person receiving an _____ shock from a filter.

*

— — — — — — — — — — — — — —

safety

electric

4-37. Another purpose of the bleeder is to keep a *minimal current* through the filter when the load is removed. This *prevents surges* when loads are reconnected. The bleeder resistor prevents voltage _____ when loads are connected.

*

— — — — — — — — — — — — — —

surges

4-38.   The *voltage divider* is a large, tapped resistor generally
inserted near the filter, like this.

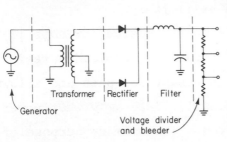

Transformer | Rectifier | Filter

Generator

Voltage divider
and bleeder

The voltage divider drops the *total
voltage*, and desired portions of this
voltage can be *tapped off* and distributed as needed. When the voltage divider
is used in this position, a separate
bleeder *is not* required because the
reactive components can _____

through the _____ _____.
*

— — — — — — — — — — — — —

discharge
voltage divider

4-39.   Take another look at the circuit in frame 3-38. This *sum-
marizes* our power system from _____ to _____ _____.
*

— — — — — — — — — — — — —

generator
voltage divider

4-40.   The *generator* is the ac _____.
*

— — — — — — — — — — — —

source

4-41.   The ac enters our equipment, and the *transformer* alters it to a usable _____ .

*
— — — — — — — — — — — — — — —

amplitude

_____

4-42.   The *rectifier* changes the ac to a _____ ____ .

*
— — — — — — — — — — — — — — —

pulsating dc

_____

4-43.   The *filter* reduces the ac _____ in the dc.

*
— — — — — — — — — — — — — — —

ripple

_____

4-44.   The *voltage divider* divides the voltage among the _____ .

*
— — — — — — — — — — — — — — —

loads

_____

4-45.   The *voltage multiplier* is not shown. It would be immediately after the rectifier if we needed a very _____ dc voltage.

*
— — — — — — — — — — — — — — —

large

4-46. Some *critical* circuits are highly *sensitive* to any variation in supply voltage. For these circuits, we need a *voltage regulator*. The voltage regulator will prevent _____ in supply voltage.
*

— — — — — — — — — — — — — — — —

variations

4-47. Relatively *quick changes* in voltage amplitude are removed by the *filter*, but the _____ cannot react to gradual changes.
*

— — — — — — — — — — — — — — — —

filter

4-48. The ac *line voltage* may be as low as 110V or as high as 130V at different times of the day. These are _____ changes that cannot be _____ by the filter.
*

— — — — — — — — — — — — — — — —

gradual
removed

4-49. The voltage regulator takes up where the filter leaves off and *automatically adjusts* the voltage to the proper level. The _____ _____ complements the filter and automatically _____ voltage levels.
*

— — — — — — — — — — — — — — — —

voltage regulator
adjusts

4-50. The simplest form of *shunt regulation* is a variable resistor parallel to the load.

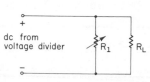

By adjusting R_1 to *bypass* more or less current, the voltage drop across R_L can be maintained at a _____ value despite changes in the circuit.

*

— — — — — — — — — — — —

constant

4-51. Suppose that R_L needs 100V and the input voltage rises by 2 volts. We *decrease* the resistance of R_1 and cause an *increase* in current through R_1. The higher current causes *more voltage* to drop across the *previous* circuits. If the adjustment is timely and proper, the 2V rise is *cancelled* completely, and the voltage across R_L remains constant at _____ volts.

*

— — — — — — — — — — — —

100

4-52. If the input *decreases*, R_1 is *increased*, and total circuit current is *decreased*. With less current, the *previous* circuits drop _____ voltage which allows the voltage across _____ to remain at 100 volts.

*

— — — — — — — — — — — —

less

R_L

4-53. A *changing* load can also affect the voltage level. This too can be *counteracted* by changing R_1. Since there are no pure parallel circuits, a change in load current will change the _____ _____ along the line.

*

voltage drop

4-54. If load current *increases*, input voltage tends to *decrease* because of more _____ _____ in the line. Increasing R_1 decreases the total current and _____ the increase in the load.

*

voltage drop
counteracts

4-55. If the variable resistor could react *quickly and automatically*, it could keep a _____ voltage across the load.

*

constant

Zener Diode Shunt

4-56. This is the same circuit that we used before when discussing the *zener diode*.

R_1 represents the *composite* line resistance, and the variable resistor has been replaced by a _____ _____ .

*

zener diode

4-57. This *zener diode* is our automatic, quick acting, *variable resistor*. The *voltage* at point A can be affected by an increase or decrease in load _____ or an increase or decrease in input _____.
*

current

voltage

4-58. If input voltage *increases*, the zener diode *conducts more*. This causes _____ voltage drop across R_1 and keeps the load voltage _____.
*

more

constant

4-59. When input voltage *decreases*, the diode *conducts less* and causes _____ voltage to be dropped across _____. This keeps the load voltage constant.
*

less

R_1

4-60. When load current *increases*, this tends to cause *more* voltage drop across R_1. The zener diode current *decreases* by the same amount that the load current increases. The current through, and voltage across, R_1 remains _____ which keeps the _____ voltage constant.

*

— — — — — — — — — — — — — — —

constant
load

4-61. When load current *decreases*, this tends to cause *less* voltage drop across R_1. The zener diode current *increases* by the same amount that load current decreases. This keeps the current through, and voltage across, R_1 at a _____ value which keeps the load voltage at a _____ value.

*

— — — — — — — — — — — — — —

constant
constant

4-62. What happens when we have a circuit where current *exceeds the capacity* of the zener diode? We use *several* zeners as parallel shunts.

The three zeners now conduct and react in *unison*, and we have _____ our shunt current capacity.

*

— — — — — — — — — — — — — —

tripled

4-63.   The *thermistor* has more current *capacity* than the zener and is sometimes used for a shunt.

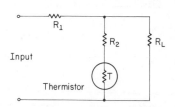

The thermistor shunt is sensitive. It regulates over a wider range of voltages and can handle _____ current than the zener.

*

— — — — — — — — — — — —

more

4-64.   The word thermistor was coined from *thermal resistor*. It is *heat* sensitive but has a *negative* temperature coefficient. When the thermistor temperature rises, its resistance _____ and its conductance _____ .

*

— — — — — — — — — — — —

decreases
increases

4-65.   Since temperature *increases* with current, the thermistor
needs a *resistor* in series with it.

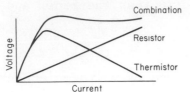

The positive temperature coefficient of the
resistor counters the _____ temperature coefficient of the _____ .

*

— — — — — — — — — — — — — — — —

negative

thermistor

4-66.   The resistor *cancels* some of the sensitivity but _____
_____ the regulation range.

*

— — — — — — — — — — — — — — — —

broadens (increases)

Electronic Shunt

4-67.   The electronic shunt is a more *sophisticated* regulator, and
it provides an *adjustment* on the level of regulated voltage.

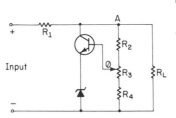

The zener diode controls the voltage on the
_____ of the transistor.

*

— — — — — — — — — — — — — — — —

emitter

4-68. The *setting* of the adjustable resistor, R_3, controls the potential on the transistor _____ .

*

— — — — — — — — — — — — — — — — —

base

4-69. The *difference* in potential between emitter and base is the input bias. This bias controls the _____ of the transistor.

*

— — — — — — — — — — — — — — — — —

conduction

4-70. The transistor is our *variable* _____ resistor.

*

— — — — — — — — — — — — — — — — —

shunt

4-71. The resistive shunt (R_2, R_3, and R_4) allows *very little* current in that branch. Its primary function is to develop a potential for the _____ of the transistor.

*

— — — — — — — — — — — — — — — — —

base

4-72. R_3 is *adjusted* until the voltage across R_L is the exact value desired. The shunt will now react to any _____ in potential at point A.

*

— — — — — — — — — — — — — — — — —

change

4-73. Assuming that point A is 100 volts, a 2 volt *increase* at the input *increases* the potential at point A by ____ volts.

*

— — — — — — — — — — — — —

2

4-74. About *half* of the increase at point A is felt on the base of the transistor. This increases forward bias by ____ volt.

*

— — — — — — — — — — — — —

one

4-75. The *increased* forward bias causes the transistor to draw *more current*. The increased current causes _____ voltage drop across R_1.

*

— — — — — — — — — — — — —

more

4-76. The increased voltage drop across R_1, in this case, is 2 volts which *cancels* the original 2 volt _____ .

*

— — — — — — — — — — — — —

increase

4-77. A *decrease* at point A, for any reason, sets up the *opposite reaction*. The transistor conducts *less*, R_1 drops ____ voltage, and point A moves back to its proper value.

*

— — — — — — — — — — — — —

less

4-78.   Since current is required to operate the regulator and this current *bypasses* the load, the shunt regulator *wastes* a certain amount of energy.   For this reason, it is used in areas where both shunt and load currents are of a *low value*.   Shunt regulators _____ energy because the operating current _____ the load.
*

—— —— —— —— —— —— —— —— —— —— —— ——

waste
bypasses

4-79.   Where *larger currents* are involved, a *series* regulator is more efficient than the _____ regulator.
*

—— —— —— —— —— —— —— —— —— —— —— ——

shunt

SERIES REGULATION

4-80.   The basic principle is a *variable resistor in series* with the load.

The input voltage is divided between the regulator resistor and the _____ _____.

*

—— —— —— —— —— —— —— —— —— —— —— ——

load resistor

4-81. The regulator resistor can be *varied* to maintain a *constant voltage* at point A regardless of input and circuit changes. When the input *increases*, *increasing* the regulator resistance _____ the voltage drop across the _____ . This keeps load voltage constant.

*

— — — — — — — — — — — — — —

increases

regulator

4-82. A *decrease* in input can be cancelled by *decreasing* the resistance of the _____ and dropping _____ voltage across it.

*

— — — — — — — — — — — — — —

regulator

less

4-83. A *decrease* in load current tends to drop _____ voltage across the regulator. _____ the resistance of the regulator cancels this action.

*

— — — — — — — — — — — — — —

less

Increasing

4-84. An *increase* in load current tends to drop _____ voltage
across the regulator. This can be cancelled by _____ the
regulator resistance.
*

more
decreasing

4-85. If the series resistor could *detect* changes and *automatically*
vary its own resistance, this would be a good voltage regulator.
The voltage regulator must _____ and automatically react to
_____ in potential.
*

detect
changes

Electronic Series Regulator

4-86. The transistor is a *variable resistor*. It can also _____
and automatically react to _____ in potential.
*

detect
changes

4-87. If we replace our variable resistor with a *transistor*, the circuit could look like this.

The transistor is now the _____ resistor in series with the _____ .

*

― ― ― ― ― ― ― ― ― ― ― ― ―

variable

load

4-88. The zener diode *holds* the transistor base at a relatively *high* potential. Any *change* of potential at point A alters the _____ bias on the transistor.

*

― ― ― ― ― ― ― ― ― ― ― ― ―

forward

4-89. An *increase* at point A *decreases* the forward bias and *reduces* transistor current. The internal resistance is inversely proportional to current. So, when conduction *decreases*, voltage drop across the transistor _____ . This leaves less voltage at point A and _____ the original increase.

*

― ― ― ― ― ― ― ― ― ― ― ― ―

increases

cancels

4-90. A *decrease* at point A sets up an *opposite reaction*. Conduction _____, resistance _____ , and voltage drop
across the transistor _____ and cancels the original decrease.
*

— — — — — — — — — — — — — — —

increases
decreases
decreases

_____

4-91. Any *change* of either input voltage or load current will effectively cause either an increase or decrease at point A. This regulator then can _____ and _____ compensate for any
change of potential.
*

— — — — — — — — — — — — — — —

detect
automatically

Adjustable Series Regulator

_____

4-92. Electronic regulators are *usually* more elaborate than that in
frame 4-87. Here is one with the *adjustable* feature.

This regulator is not only adjustable, it
is a much better regulator than those
shown previously. It is *stable* over a
wide range of voltages and currents and
maintains regulation within a *very close
tolerance*. The series, variable resistor
in this regulator has been replaced by ____ .
*

— — — — — — — — — — — — — — —

Q_1

_____

167

4-93. Again, point A is the spot where we want a *regulated* voltage. Any change of input _____ or load _____ will tend to change the potential at this point.

*

— — — — — — — — — — — — —

potential

current

4-94. The key to this regulator is the *bias on Q_1*. It is *forward* biased across the emitter-base junction. Changing this bias will change its internal _____ and the _____ _____ across it.

*

— — — — — — — — — — — — —

resistance

voltage drop

4-95. The bias on Q_1 is *controlled* by the conduction of Q_2. The *conduction* of Q_2 is, in turn, controlled by the potential at _____ _.

*

— — — — — — — — — — — — —

point A

4-96. The zener diode couples the *total change* to the emitter of Q_2, and the resistive network couples *about half* of the change to the _____ .

*

— — — — — — — — — — — — —

base

4-97. When point A becomes *more positive*, it *decreases* the forward bias on Q_2. Q_2 conducts *less*; the voltage across it _____ and places a _____ positive potential on the base of Q_1.
*

increases
higher

4-98. Q_1 is a PNP transistor, and the *increased positive* on its base reduces the forward bias. Q_1 conducts _____ and the voltage drop across it _____ .
*

less
increases

4-99. The *increased* voltage drop across Q_1 cancels the original increase at _____ __.
*

point A

4-100. A *decrease* at point A triggers a *reverse action*. Forward bias on Q_2 *increases*, voltage drop across Q_2 *decreases*, and forward bias on Q_1 *increases*. Q_1 conducts more; the voltage drop across Q_1 _____ , allowing an _____ in potential at point A to cancel the original _____ .
*

decreases
increase
decrease

169

4-101. Bias on Q_2 is *adjustable* by moving the center arm of R_3. This is a *screwdriver adjustment*. Moving the arm toward R_2 *reduces* the forward bias on Q_2 and causes a _____ in the regulated voltage at point A.
*

— — — — — — — — — — — — —

decrease

___

4-102. Moving the arm of R_3 toward R_4 *increases* the forward bias on Q_2 and causes an _____ in regulated voltage at point A.
*

— — — — — — — — — — — — —

increase

___

4-103. Some regulators are specified as *current regulators* and others as *voltage regulators*. We have analyzed these from a voltage standpoint, but when you control *either* voltage or current, the other takes care of itself. A voltage regulator or a current regulator actually regulates both _____ and _____ .
*

— — — — — — — — — — — — —

voltage

current

SUMMARY

1. *Voltage multipliers* are used with circuits which require very *high* voltage and very *low* current.
2. Adding a *diode section* to a cascade voltage *doubler* changes it to a voltage *tripler*. Other sections can be added to further increase the *multiplication factor*.

3. *Filtering* is a process of reducing the ac ripple in a pulsating dc.

4. The *capacitor input filter* is effective with low to moderate current.

5. For loads with high or changing currents, it is necessary to use *full-wave rectifiers* with *choke input filters*.

6. The *bleeder resistor* provides a discharge path for the filter when the loads are disconnected.

7. *Voltage regulation* is the process of maintaining voltage at a constant amplitude.

8. The principles of *shunt regulation* are demonstrated by a variable resistor parallel to the load.

9. A *zener diode shunt* is an effective regulator for low currents.

10. The voltage regulator *senses and compensates* for any change of input potential and any change in load current.

11. The *thermistor* in series with a resistor makes a good shunt regulator.

12. The *electronic shunt* regulator uses a transistor and a zener diode. It also provides an *adjustment* for the level of regulated voltage.

13. Shunt regulators *waste* energy because the operating current *bypasses* the load.

14. A *variable resistor in series* with the load demonstrates the principles of series regulation.

15. The *electronic series regulator* uses a transistor for the variable resistor.

16. Changing the conduction of a *transistor* changes its internal resistance.

17. When adjusting the regulated voltage of a series regulator, moving the *arm* of the potentiometer to a *more positive* point *reduces* the regulated voltage.

18. Regulating *either* current or voltage automatically regulates *both*.

19. The series regulator is more *efficient* because its operating current is the same as the load current.

SECTION 5
AMPLIFICATION

Amplification is a process which *increases the magnitude* of a signal. About 50% of *all* electronic circuits produce some amplification. In many cases, amplification is the *primary* purpose of the stage. Sometimes the stage is designed for other tasks and produces amplification as a *by-product*. Amplifier stages are designed to *concentrate* on any component of the signal: *current*, *voltage*, or *power*.

AMPLIFICATION PRINCIPLES

5-1. Any circuit which produces an output larger than the input is an *amplifier*. An amplifier *increases the magnitude* of a signal to produce an output that is _____ than the input.
*

— — — — — — — — — — — — —

larger

5-2. Amplifiers are designed to *concentrate* on one or more of the components of a signal. *Power amplifiers* increase _____ , current amplifiers increase _____ , and voltage amplifiers increase _____ .

*
— — — — — — — — — — — — — — — — —

power
current
voltage

Biasing

5-3. The *triode transistor* is the vehicle we will use in our amplifier stages. When properly connected and properly biased, this transistor can *amplify* either voltage, _____ , or _____ , and in some cases, all three at the same time.

*
— — — — — — — — — — — — — — — — —

current
power

5-4. According to previous information, a *conducting* transistor must have _____ bias across the emitter-base junction and _____ bias across the collector-base junction.

*
— — — — — — — — — — — — — — — — —

forward
reverse

5-5. The *polarities* for proper bias are exactly opposite for the NPN and PNP transistors. The *first letter* in the transistor designator shows the proper *emitter polarity with respect to the base* for establishing forward bias across this junction. Forward bias on the input of the NPN places the emitter more _____ than the base; for the PNP, the emitter is more _____ than the base.

*

—— —— —— —— —— —— —— —— —— —— —— —— ——

negative
positive

5-6. The *second letter* in the transistor indicator shows the proper *collector polarity with respect to the base* for establishing reverse bias across this junction. Reverse bias on the NPN places the collector more _____ than the base; for the PNP, the collector is more _____ than the base.

*

—— —— —— —— —— —— —— —— —— —— —— —— ——

positive
negative

5-7. These transistors are *properly* biased.

NPN   PNP

Both transistors have _____ bias across the input junction and _____ bias across the output junction.

*

—— —— —— —— —— —— —— —— —— —— —— —— ——

forward
reverse

5-8. Remember that we are dealing with *electron flow* as current.
In both types of transistors, total current exists in the *emitter* in
a direction _____ the arrow. *In the NPN*, current *enters* through
the emitter and emerges by way of base and _____ .
*

— — — — — — — — — — — — — — — —

against
collector

5-9. *In the PNP*, current *enters* through the base and _____
and emerges through the _____ .
*

— — — — — — — — — — — — — — — —

collector
emitter

5-10. *Reverse bias* of any level across the input junction will cut
the transistor off. While cut off, there is a small *leakage* current
in the reverse direction. In most cases, the leakage can be completely *ignored*. The transistor is cut off by _____ bias.
During cut off, the only current is a minute _____ current in
the reverse direction.
*

— — — — — — — — — — — — — — — —

reverse
leakage

5-11. The input junction bias is *increased and decreased* by an amount equal to the peak amplitude of the input signal. The *small change* of input bias causes a *large change* at the collector. Input bias is _____ by the input signal, and a small change of input bias causes a large change at the _____ .
*
—— — — — — — — — — — — — —

varied (changed)
collector

5-12. If the signal is *too large*, it can either *saturate* the transistor or *cut it off*; sometimes both. As cut off or saturation is approached, the output signal becomes *distorted*. For a good *reproduction* of the input signal, the signal must be small enough to avoid both _____ ___ and _____ .
*
—— — — — — — — — — — — — —

cut off
saturation

Types of Amplifiers

5-13. Amplifiers are *named* according to the *frequencies* of the signals that they amplify: *audio*, *video*, *intermediate*, and *radio*. The *audio amplifier* amplifies signals with frequencies in the _____ range.
*
—— — — — — — — — — — — — —

audio

5-14. *Gain* is a general expression for a *ratio* of output amplitude to input amplitude. Gain = output/input. A gain of 100 indicates that the output signal is _____ times as large as the input signal.

*

— — — — — — — — — — — — — — — —

100

5-15. Even when the output is *less* than the input, it is still called *gain*. A gain of 0.5 indicates that the output is just _____ the size of the input.

*

— — — — — — — — — — — — — — — —

half

5-16. When dealing with *power* amplification, the gain is often expressed in *decibels* (dB). For our purposes, a gain of 3 dB (increase) indicates that power has been *doubled*. It doubles again for each *multiple* of 3 dB. A power gain of 9 dB indicates an output power which is _____ times as large as the input power.

*

— — — — — — — — — — — — — — — —

eight

5-17. A power gain of *negative decibels* actually shows a power loss. For each gain of -3 dB the input power is *reduced by half*. A power gain of -9 dB indicates that the output power is _____ the size of the input power.

*

— — — — — — — — — — — — — — — —

one-eighth

5-18. Any reference to gain implies *amplification* of the ac signal. Therefore, the ratio is actually the _____ in output divided by the _____ in input.

*

— — — — — — — — — — — — —

change

change

5-19. A two volt change at the input produces a 30 volt change at the output. What is the gain?

*

— — — — — — — — — — — — —

30/2 = 15

5-20. A one milliampere change at the input causes a 0.9 mA change at the output. What is the gain?

*

— — — — — — — — — — — — —

0.9/1 = 0.9

5-21. A 5 μA change at the input produces a 5 mA change in the output. What is the gain?

*

— — — — — — — — — — — — —

5 mA/5 μA = 1000

5-22. The power is calculated by ac effective values of voltage and current. Input power is E_{in} x I_{in}; output power is _____ .

*

— — — — — — — — — — — — —

E_{out} x I_{out}

5-23. The amplifier *class* indicates the percentage of the *total time* that the transistor is *conducting*. The *four* classes are A, AB, B, and C. The transistor conduction _____ is indicated by the amplifier _____ .

*

— — — — — — — — — — — — —

time

class

5-24. A class A amplifier conducts *all the time* (100%). The class B conducts *half the time* (50%). With each sine wave input, the class A amplifier will produce one _____ _____ in the output; the class B will produce one _____ .

*

— — — — — — — — — — — — —

sine wave

alternation

5-25. The class AB amplifier conducts *more than the B* but *less than the A*. A sine wave into this amplifier will produce a partial sine wave out. The output will be *more than 180 degrees* but less than _____ degrees.

*

— — — — — — — — — — — — —

360

5-26. The class C amplifier conducts *less than 50% of the time.*
A 360 degree sine wave into a class C amplifier will produce an output less than _____ degrees.
*

— — — — — — — — — — — — —

180

5-27. This drawing illustrates the effect of amplifying a sine wave
through *each of the four classes.*

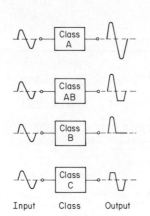

Input   Class   Output

No class is *best* for all applications. The best
reproduction of the input is provided by class
_____ . The best job of changing a *sine wave to
a square wave* is performed by class _____.

*

— — — — — — — — — — — — —

A
C

5-28.   A *signal* is a wave *variation* with respect to time.   All of these wave shapes and many others are used as signals.

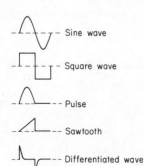
— Sine wave

— Square wave

— Pulse

— Sawtooth

— Differentiated wave

The full range of signals includes *nearly all* wave shapes because they all have some _____ with respect to _____ .

*

— — — — — — — — — — — — — — — —

variation

time

5-29.   The signal *source* is always the *previous stage*.   It may have generated the signal or it may have merely passed it along, but we think of it as an *ac generator*.   To any electronic circuit, the signal source is the _____ _____ .

*

— — — — — — — — — — — — — — — —

previous stage

5-30. *All* triode transistor amplifiers fall into *three configurations: common base, common emitter,* and *common collector*. The configuration indicates the *element* that is common to *input and output*. The *common base* is connected so that the _____ is common to input and output. The collector of the _____ _____ is common to input and output.

*

–– –– –– –– –– –– –– –– –– –– ––

base
common collector

5-31. Sometimes the three configurations are referred to as *grounded base, grounded emitter,* and *grounded collector*. We use *common* instead of *ground* because it is more descriptive. A grounded emitter amplifier is the same circuit as a _____ _____ amplifier.

*

–– –– –– –– –– –– –– –– –– –– ––

common emitter

5-32. This is the *common base* configuration for both types of transistors. The circuits are properly biased.

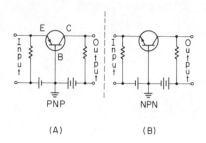

PNP (A)   NPN (B)

Both circuits have the input across the _____ junction and output across the _____ junction.

*

—— —— —— —— —— —— —— —— —— —— ——

emitter-base
collector-base

5-33. Circuit A in frame 5-32 is identical to circuit B *except* that all polarities are _____ .

*

—— —— —— —— —— —— —— —— —— —— ——

reversed

5-34.   Battery bias is *seldom* used except in small, portable equipment.   A more *likely source* of bias voltage is the voltage divider
of the power system.   Replacing our batteries with the voltage
divider, we have a circuit similar to this.

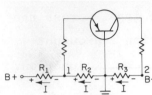

This is a _____ type transistor, and R$_1$, R$_2$
and R$_3$ comprise the _____ _____ .

PNP
voltage divider

5-35.   Instead of showing the voltage divider, the bias voltages
are *designated* on the schematic.   Most schematics show neither
battery nor _____ _____ but _____ the bias voltages.

voltage divider
designate

5-36. A *dc voltage* will be designated by V. V_{BB} will be the *base supply* voltage, V_{CC} will be the *collector supply* voltage, and V_{EE} will be the *emitter supply* voltage. This is the same circuit as in frame 5-34.

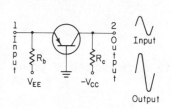

The *input bias* is the positive potential from V_{EE} to _____ . The *output bias* is the _____ potential from $-V_{CC}$ to _____ .

*

— — — — — — — — — — — —

ground

negative

ground

5-37. The input signal is applied *between* point 1 and V_{EE}. The output is taken *between* point 2 and $-V_{CC}$. We may assume that there is an *ac ground* at any point where a signal circuit joins a dc circuit. This ground is generally provided by ac bypass _____ .
Without the ac ground, the signal would hamper voltage _____ .
*

— — — — — — — — — — — —

capacitors

regulation

5-38. Here are some *typical values* for a common base circuit.

  1. Input resistance (INTERNAL) 30 to 150 ohms.
  2. Output resistance (INTERNAL) 300 to 500 kohms.
  3. Voltage gain 300 to 1500.
  4. Current gain less than unity.
  5. Power gain 20 to 30 dB.

This amplifier provides a strong _____ gain, a reasonable power gain, and suffers a decrease in _____ .

*

— — — — — — — — — — — — —

voltage
current

5-39. Static characteristic *curves* are provided for the *common base* configuration by transistor manufacturers. Each transistor has *its own* set of curves, but all curves have many common features. There is a separate set of characteristic curves for each type of

_____ . Static curves for the transistor in a _____ _____ configuration can be obtained from the manufacturer.

*

— — — — — — — — — — — — —

transistor
common base

5-40. This is a *sample family* of characteristic curves for one
transistor in a *common base* configuration.

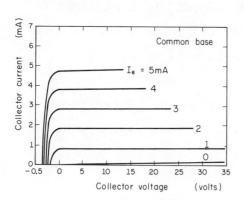

This chart shows the relationship of
_____ current and _____
current for all reasonable values of
_____ voltage.

*

― ― ― ― ― ― ― ― ― ― ― ―

emitter
collector
collector

5-41. Maximum *current gain* for this configuration is sometimes
supplied along with the curves. If not, it is easily *calculated*
from chart values. Maximum current gain is symbolized by alpha (α).
The *formula* is $\alpha = \Delta I_c / \Delta I_e$ with collector voltage constant. Values
for this formula can be taken from the _____ _____ .
The calculation reveals the _____ _____ gain for this transistor in a common base configuration.
*

― ― ― ― ― ― ― ― ― ― ― ―

characteristic curves
maximum current

5-42. On the chart in frame 5-40, move up the 20 volt line to an I_e of 2 mA. The collector current for this point is about 1.9 mA. Move up the 20 volt line again to I_e of 3 mA. ΔI_e is 1 mA (3 mA – 2 mA). The collector current is now about 2.85 mA. ΔI_c is 0.95 mA (2.85 mA – 1.9 mA). Substituting into the formula we have α = 0.95/1. α = 0.95. Approximately this same result can be obtained for *any value* of collector voltage from 5 volts to 30 volts. These figures verify the fact that the _____ ____ configuration always has a current gain less than _____ .

*
—— —— —— —— —— —— —— —— —— —— —— —— ——

common base
unity

5-43. Previously we mentioned input and output resistances as being *internal*. The input resistance is the resistance across the *input junction*. The output resistance is the resistance across the *output junction*. These values of resistance are *independent* of circuit components and are measured with the *external leads open*. Input and output resistances are characteristic resistances across the input and output _____ .

*
—— —— —— —— —— —— —— —— —— —— —— —— ——

junctions

5-44.   Here are *both* types of transistors in a *common emitter* configuration.

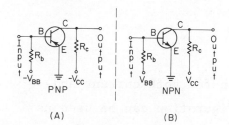

PNP   (A)   NPN   (B)

This circuit gets its name from the fact that the _____ is common to _____ and _____ .

*

--- --- --- --- --- --- --- --- --- ---

emitter

input

output

5-45.   In *both* circuits the *input* junction (emitter-base) is *forward biased*.   In the PNP, a *positive* going signal opposes input bias and causes a *negative* swing at the collector.   In the NPN, a *positive* signal aids input bias and causes a *negative* swing at the collector. Both types of transistors in the common _____ configuration produce a _____ degree phase shift between input and output.
*

--- --- --- --- --- --- --- --- --- ---

emitter

180

5-46. Here are some *typical values* for a common emitter configuration.

     1.   Input resistance 500 to 1500 ohms.

     2.   Output resistance 30 to 50 kohms.

     3.   Voltage gain 300 to 1000.

     4.   Current gain 25 to 50.

     5.   Power gain 25 to 40 dB.

The *voltage gain* is only fair, but the gain for both current and power are considered excellent. This configuration can be used as a voltage amplifier, a _____ amplifier, or a _____ amplifier.

*

current

power

5-47. Static characteristic curves are also available for the *common emitter*. Here is a sample family.

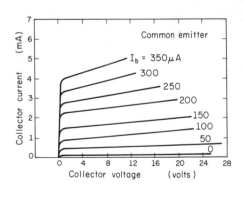

This chart shows the relationship of _____ current and _____ current for various values of _____ voltage.

*

collector

base

collector

190

5-48. Beta (β) symbolizes maximum *current gain* for the *common emitter*, and $\beta = \Delta I_c / \Delta I_b$. This formula is true for any constant value of collector voltage. β may be obtained from the manufacturer or *calculated* by using values from the _____ _____ .

*

— — — — — — — — — — — — — —

characteristic curves

5-49. Taking a set of values from the 12 volt line in frame 5-47, start at the intersection of 12V and I_b of 200 μA. At this point, I_b = 200 μA and I_c = 2.65 mA. Move up the line to I_b = 250 μA. The I_c is now 3.25 mA. I_b = 50 μA and I_c = 0.6 mA. $\beta = 0.6 \times 10^{-3}/50 \times 10^{-6}$. β = _____ , and this is the maximum _____ _____ for this transistor in the common base configuration at this value of collector voltage.

*

— — — — — — — — — — — — — —

12

current gain

5-50. For *higher* values of collector voltage, the I_b lines *spread out* to a certain extent. This means that a higher collector voltage provides a slightly higher _____ _____ .

*

— — — — — — — — — — — — — —

current gain

5-51. This drawing shows *both* types of transistors in the *common collector* configuration.

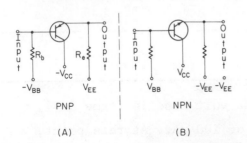

PNP

(A)

NPN

(B)

In both circuits, the input is across the _____ junction, and the output is across the _____ _____ junction.

*

— — — — — — — — — —

collector-base
collector-emitter

5-52. A *positive* going signal into the PNP *opposes* the input bias and causes a *positive swing* in the output. A *positive* going signal into the NPN aids the input bias and causes a *positive swing* in the output. In both cases, the input and output signals are ___ _____ with each other.

*

— — — — — — — — — —

in phase

5-53. Here are some *typical figures* for a common collector configuration.

    1.   Input resistance 30 to 500 ohms.

    2.   Output resistance 500 to 1000 ohms.

    3.   Voltage gain less than unity.

    4.   Current gain 25 to 50.

    5.   Power gain 10 to 20 dB.

Current gain is excellent, power gain is _____ , and there is a loss in _____ amplitude.

*

———————————————————————————————————

fair

voltage

5-54. The *common collector* may be used for either a _____ amplifier or a _____ amplifier.

*

———————————————————————————————————

current

power

5-55. As a _____ amplifier, the common collector *compares* favorably with the common emitter.

*

———————————————————————————————————

current

5-56. As a _____ amplifier, the common emitter is *better than* the common collector.

*

— — — — — — — — — — — — — — — — —

power

___

5-57. The common collector is found most often in areas where *impedance matching* is a problem. Its *high* input resistance and low output resistance helps in matching a _____ impedance to a _____ impedance.

*

— — — — — — — — — — — — — — — — —

high
low

___

5-58. There *is no* separate family of static characteristic curves for the common collector. The *common emitter* chart also serves the common collector. There is no established symbol for maximum current gain, but it is *equivalent* to $\Delta I_e / \Delta I_b$ with a constant value of collector voltage. There are no separate _____ _____ nor symbol for maximum _____ _____.

*

— — — — — — — — — — — — — — — — —

characteristic curves
current gain

___

5-59. The *common emitter* family of curves also serves the _____ _____.

*

— — — — — — — — — — — — — — — — —

common collector

___

5-60. Maximum current gain for the common collector is _____
with the collector voltage constant.

*
- - - - - - - - - - - - - - - -

$\Delta I_e / \Delta I_b$

5-61. Taking values from the chart in frame 5-47, we have no I_e
given, but I_e is *always* the sum of I_c and I_b. With collector voltage
of 6V and I_b of 250 µA, I_c is 3 mA. What is the value of I_e?

*
- - - - - - - - - - - - - - - -

$3 \times 10^{-3} + 250 \times 10^{-6} = 3.25$ mA

5-62. Move up the 6 volt line to 300 µA. I_c is now 3.67 mA and
I_e is _____ .

*
- - - - - - - - - - - - - - - -

3.67 mA + 300 µA = 3.97 mA

5-63. In frames 5-61 and 5-62, ΔI_e is 0.72 mA and ΔI_b is 50 µA.
What is the maximum current gain?

*
- - - - - - - - - - - - - - - -

$0.72 \times 10^{-3} / 50 \times 10^{-6} = 14.4$

5-64. The static characteristics show *capabilities* but not how the transistor performs in a *specific* circuit. A *load line* on a family of static curves changes the chart to a *dynamic* characteristic chart by revealing *particular* circuit performance. The _____ _____ on a family of curves reveals _____ characteristics of the transistor.
*

— — — — — — — — — — — — —

load line
dynamic

Plotting the Load Line

5-65. A load line is a *diagonal line* on a family of characteristic curves. The exact position of the line is *determined* by the size of the load resistor and the amplitude of the output bias. The _____ of output bias and the size of the _____ resistor determine the position of the _____.
*

— — — — — — — — — — — — —

amplitude
load
load line

5-66. Let's use this circuit and *plot* a load line.

This is a _____ _____ configuration, and we will use the matching characteristic chart.

Input

Output

5k Ω

20V

*

_____

common emitter

5-67. The *first step* is to determine the *maximum collector voltage and maximum collector current*. In this case, V_{CC} is 20V. With zero I_c, the full 20V appears at the *collector*. *Maximum current* is the point where I_c is strong enough to drop all of V_{CC} across the collector load resistor. This is 5 kΩ and 20V which gives us 4 mA. The maximum collector voltage for this circuit is ____ volts at _____ mA of I_c. The maximum current is ____ mA when collector voltage is _____ volts.

*

_____

20
zero
4
zero

197

5-68. We now have *two* points to mark on the chart: *zero volts with 4 mA* and *20 volts with zero mA*. This chart shows the two points *plotted* and connected with a straight line.

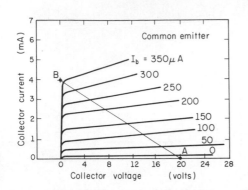

Points A and B represent *two extreme* conditions. Point A is maximum

_____ _____, and point B is

maximum _____ _____.

*

— — — — — — — — — — — — — — — —

collector voltage
collector current

5-69. The *diagonal line* connecting the two extreme conditions is the *load line*. It represents *all possible values* of _____ current, _____ voltage, and base current for this transistor and a _____ kΩ load resistor.

*

— — — — — — — — — — — — — — — —

collector
collector
5

5-70.   Input bias will establish an *operating point* some place along this load line.   Our operating point should be *near the center* of the load line; let's say the point where it intersects I_b of 200 µA. If we have a V_{BB} of 20V, what size R_b do we need to *establish* a base current of 200 µA?

*

R_b = 20/200 x 10^{-6} = 100kΩ

5-71.   In some cases, the input resistance must be considered, but here, it is in series with R_b.   The typical input resistance of 500 to 1500 ohms is of *no consequence* because R_b is so large by comparison. The bias is *principally* established by I_b through _____ .

*

R_b

5-72.   This drawing shows the completed circuit.

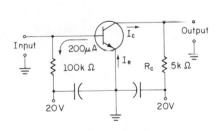

There is a voltage drop of _____ volts across R_b which provides the desired base current of _____ µA.

*

20

200

5-73.   The desired *operating point* has been established on the load
line.   It is point C on this chart.

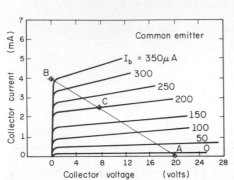

The operating point indicates the circuit conditions when there is *no signal
input*.   In this case, I_b is _____ μA,
I_c is _____ mA, and collector voltage
is ___ volts.

*
— — — — — — — — — — — — — — — — — —

200

2.4

8

5-74.   An incoming signal will *vary the bias* and set up ac variations
along the load line.   The *swing* will be in both directions from the
_____ _____.

*
— — — — — — — — — — — — — — — — — —

operating point

5-75. The incoming signal is applied across R_b, but the manner of
application places R_b in *parallel* with the input resistance.

R_b is so large that a small signal has
practically no effect, but the full
signal is also across the small input
resistor. In this case, the 0.05V
peak to peak input signal causes a
_____ µA variation in the emitter to base current.

Input resistance
500 Ω

0.05V R_b 100kΩ

*

0.05V/500Ω = 100

5-76. Back to the *load line* in frame 5-73, this 100 µA *swing* of
input current goes up the load line to 250 µA, back to 200 µA, down
the load line to 150 µA, and back to 200 µA. This swing occurs with
each sine wave of the input signal. The swing of I_b causes a corresponding swing in _____ current and _____ voltage.

*

collector
collector

5-77. When I_b is 150 µA, I_c is _____ mA and collector voltage is
_____ volts.

*

1.7
11.2

5-78. When I_b is 250 μA, I_c is _____ mA and collector voltage is
       _____ volts.

*

2.9

5.5

5-79. The 0.05 volt input signal has caused a *swing* of _____ μA in
I_b, _____ mA in I_c, and _____ volts in collector voltage.

*

100

1.2

5.7

5-80. Current gain is $\Delta I_c / \Delta I_b$. This amplifier has a current gain
of _____ .

*

12

5-81. *Voltage gain* is the change in collector voltage divided by
the change in signal voltage. The voltage gain is _____ .

*

114

5-82. *Power gain* is equivalent to current gain times voltage gain. The power gain is _____ .

*

— — — — — — — — — — — — — —

1568

5-83. The *gain* of a particular transistor is greatly *affected* by the *size* of the load resistor. This chart shows a different load line for each of *three* different load resistors.

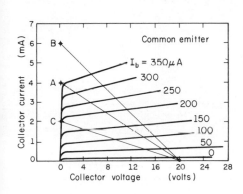

Line B is for an R_c of 3.3 kΩ.

Line C is for an R_c of 10 kΩ.

Line A is the same as our previous load line for an R_c of ___ kΩ.

*

— — — — — — — — — — — — — —

5

5-84. *Which is best?* That depends on the type of amplifier we want to construct. The large load resistor (B) provides more *current gain*. The small resistor provides the greatest *voltage gain*. Voltage gain is _____ proportional to the value of R_c, and current gain is _____ proportional to the same value.

*

— — — — — — — — — — — — — —

inversely
directly

203

5-85. Changing the output *bias* has *very little* effect on the *gain*. Here are *three* load lines; one for each of three different values of *collector voltage*.

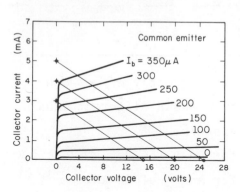

Line A is our previous load line for a collector voltage of 20 volts. Line B shows a collector voltage of ____volts, and line C is for ____ volts.

*
___ ___ ___ ___ ___ ___ ___ ___ ___ ___ ___ ___

25
15

5-86. As the collector voltage *increases*, the load line moves from the lower left of the chart toward the _____ _____.

*
___ ___ ___ ___ ___ ___ ___ ___ ___ ___ ___ ___

upper right

5-87. The load lines are *parallel* to one another, but the I_b lines tend to spread out at the higher voltages. Therefore, gain will _____ slightly as collector voltages increase.

*
___ ___ ___ ___ ___ ___ ___ ___ ___ ___ ___ ___

increase

5-88.   The various points along a load line may be *projected* onto a chart of *collector current vs base current*.   This drawing illustrates such a projection.   *Eleven points* along the load line on chart B have been projected to chart A.   Connecting these eleven points forms the new curve on chart A.   This curve is a *dynamic transfer characteristic curve*.

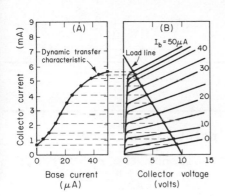

Chart A can be used to *predict* the effect this amplifier will have on any input signal.   The load line, of course, can do the same thing, but this chart is completely *current oriented* and is easier to read.   A change in base current can be converted directly into a change in

_____ _____.

*

collector current

5-89. Here is chart A with the points projected *horizontally and vertically*.

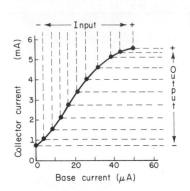

Base current (μA)

A change of *input* current is plotted between two *vertical lines*, and the change in *output* current is projected between corresponding _____ lines.

*

---

horizontal

5-90. By *changing the bias*, the operating point can be *moved* to any point on the curve. The operating point establishes the *reference*, and both input and output will swing in _____ _____ from this point.

*

---

both directions

5-91. For *input* signals, the area to the *left* of the operating point *is negative*; to the *right is positive*. For the *output* signal, the area *above the operating point* is _____ and *below the operating point* is _____ .

*

---

positive
negative

5-92. This chart shows a *distorted* output caused from the operating
point (A) being set *too low* on the curve.

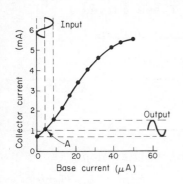

The negative swing of the input signal drives
the transistor too near _____ ___. This
results in a reduced amplification on the
_____ alternation of the output.

*

----

cut off

negative

5-93. This chart shows a *distorted* output resulting from the
operating point (A) being set *too high* on the curve.

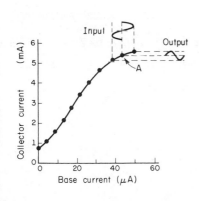

In this area, the transistor is very near
_____ , and the input signal has
little effect on the _____ _____.

*

----

saturation

collector current

5-94. A distorted output *occurs* when the operating point is set either *too high or too low* on the curve. The curved ends of the line show a *nonlinear ratio* between I_b and I_c. These curved portions must be avoided to prevent a _____ output.

*

— — — — — — — — — — — — — — — —

distorted

___

5-95. *Fidelity* is the degree of exactness to which the input is reproduced in the output. A *nondistorted* output is *high fidelity;* a *distorted* output is *low fidelity.* The circuits in frames 5-92 and 5-93 are _____ fidelity circuits.

*

— — — — — — — — — — — — — — — —

low

___

5-96. This is a *high fidelity* circuit.

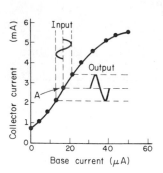

Notice that the operating point (A) has been set very near the *center of the linear portion* of the curve. This allows the full signal *swing* without distortion. The output is a good amplified _____ of the input.

*

— — — — — — — — — — — — — — — —

reproduction

5-97.   The input signal in frame 5-96 is 10 µA peak to peak.   The
output has a 1.25 mA peak to peak swing.   What is the current amplification?
*
___ __ __ __ __ __ __ __ __ __ __ __

125

Frequency Limitation

5-98.   The internal impedance of transistors *limits* their frequency
handling ability.   This drawing illustrates the internal impedance.

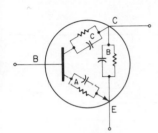

Impedance A appears across the *emitter-base*
junction, and since this is a common emitter,
it represents the *input* impedance.   Impedance B
appears between *emitter and collector*; this is
the *output* impedance.   Impedance C is across the
collector-base junction.   Impedance C provides
a path for the output signal to *couple back* to
the _____ circuit.
*
___ __ __ __ __ __ __ __ __ __ __ __

input

5-99.   At *low* frequencies, the capacitors are effectively *open*
circuits.   This makes the impedance almost pure _____ .
*
___ __ __ __ __ __ __ __ __ __ __ __

resistance

5-100. As frequencies *increase*, the capacitive reactances

_____.

*

— — — — — — — — — — — — — —

decrease

5-101. There comes a point at the *higher* frequencies when the capacitors are almost *shorts*. The *high frequency* transistors are manufactured with very *low* capacitance. The lower capacitance offers _____ capacitive reactance for a given frequency and enables the transistor to operate at _____ frequencies.

*

— — — — — — — — — — — — — —

more
higher

5-102. Transistors are rated for *maximum* collector power. This rated power *must not be exceeded* for extended periods of time. A *constant power line*, as shown here, will help to keep the power within recommended bounds.

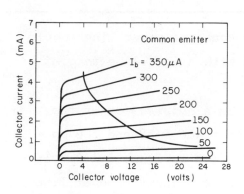

This line can be on the same chart as the load line. It connects *all the points* where voltage times current is equal to the *rated power*. Rated power must not be _____ for appreciable periods of time. The _____ _____helps to avoid too much power.

*

exceeded
constant power line

5-103. The constant power line connects *all points* where collector voltage times _____ _____ is equal to the _____ _____.
*

collector current
rated power

5-104. The constant power line in frame 5-102 was constructed for a *rated power* of 18 mW. The product of collector voltage and collector current at any point on this curve is equal to ____ mW.

*

–– –– –– –– –– –– –– –– –– –– –– ––

18

5-105. For *maximum safe* power gain, the constant power line should be drawn first, then construct a circuit with a load line *tangent* to the power curve: like this.

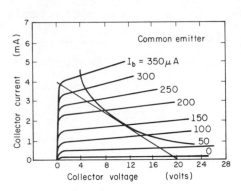

This chart is a *combination* of the *load line* in frame 5-68 and the *constant power line* in frame 5-102. If the load line *crosses* the power line, the rated power is being *exceeded*. This circuit is constructed for _____ safe power gain.

*

–– –– –– –– –– –– –– –– –– –– –– ––

maximum

5-106. Most transistors can withstand *short surges* of power far in excess of the rated power, but a _____ power in excess of the _____ value will likely destroy the transistor.

*

–– –– –– –– –– –– –– –– –– –– –– ––

constant

rated

5-107.   An amplifier is *overdriven* when the input signal drives it
to *either* saturation or cut off.   Even a properly biased amplifier
may be overdriven if the signal is *too large*.   This drawing illustrates the *result* of overdriving.

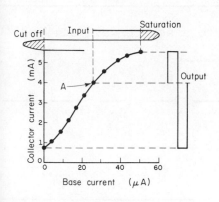

This transistor is biased to operate
near the center of the linear portion
of the curve.   Even so, the maximum
input it can handle is about 50 uA peak
to peak.   This input is about 70 uA peak
to peak.   The result is, the positive
alternation drives the amplifier to
_____ , and the negative alternation drives it to _____ _____ .

*

saturation

cut off

5-108.   The portions of the signal *above saturation and below cut off*
are eliminated from the output.   The positive alternation is *limited*
(clipped) by _____ ; the negative alternation is *limited*
(clipped) by _____ _____ .

*

saturation

cut off

213

5-109. The output is a *square wave* that shows the result of both saturation _____ and cut off _____.

*

— — — — — — — — — — — — — — — —

limiting

limiting

5-110. The *task* of converting a sine wave to a square wave can be accomplished by an _____ _____.

*

— — — — — — — — — — — — — — — —

overdriven amplifier

Self-Biasing

5-111. Only *fixed* bias has been shown up to this point, but transistors can supply their *own bias* to some extent. Here is a transistor with a *self-biased input*.

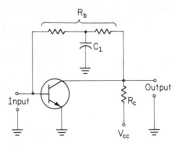

The *collector voltage* becomes the power source for the input bias. The *split resistor* (R_b) and *bypass capacitor* prevent signal feedback. Base current through R_b is established by the static (no signal) collector voltage. Input bias is equivalent to the voltage drop across _____.

*

— — — — — — — — — — — — — — — —

R_b

5-112. Transistors are sensitive to *temperature* changes. Self-biasing allows the transistor to *adjust* the bias as it reacts to changes of *temperature*. This provides a certain degree of *thermal stabilization*. Transistor characteristics change with _____ . Self bias is one method of establishing _____ _____ .
*

— — — — — — — — — — — — — — —

temperature
thermal stabilization

COUPLING NETWORKS

5-113. *Coupling networks* are used to pass signals from one stage to the next. There are *four popular types* of coupling: *direct, RC, impedance*, and *transformer*. The type selected, in any given case, is generally *dictated* by the signal frequency. The signal _____ indicates whether the coupling network should be _____ , _____ , _____ , or transformer.
*

— — — — — — — — — — — — — — —

frequency
direct, RC, impedance

5-114. *Direct coupling* is illustrated in this drawing.

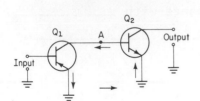

This coupling is essentially a *straight wire* from the _____ of one stage to the _____ of the next.

*

— — — — — — — — — — — —

output

input

5-115. A resistor may be connected from point A to either ground or B+. If the resistor *is not* there, the output current of Q_1 is limited to the _____ _____ of Q_2.

*

— — — — — — — — — — — —

input current

5-116. Direct coupling is used *only* with dc and very low frequency signals. One of its main disadvantages is *thermal instability*. If temperature causes a *bias change* in the first stage, it will be *amplified* and passed on to the other stages. The usefulness of direct coupling is limited by _____ _____ because of the tendency to amplify and pass on the _____ changes in bias.

*

— — — — — — — — — — — —

thermal instability

thermal

5-117. This is a drawing of *two* stages connected by *RC coupling*.

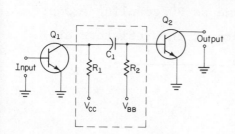

The coupling circuit is *enclosed* in broken lines. R_1 and R_2 are serving a *dual* role. R_1 is part of the coupling, but it is also the _____ resistor for Q_1. R_2 is the _____ resistor for Q_2 as well as being part of the coupling.

*

——— —— ——— —— ——— —— ——— —— ——— —— ——— ——

load

base

5-118. RC coupling is popular for *audio* frequencies. *Below* these frequencies, the capacitive reactance *blocks* the signal. *Above* these frequencies, the capacitor becomes a *short*. RC coupling is not widely used except for _____ frequencies because the capacitor _____ low frequencies and _____ high frequencies.

*

——— —— ——— —— ——— —— ——— —— ——— —— ——— ——

audio

blocks

shorts

5-119. This is *impedance* coupling.

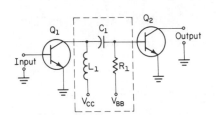

This is the same as RC coupling *except* that one or more of the resistors are replaced by an _____ .

*

— — — — — — — — — — — — — —

inductor

5-120. At very *low* frequencies, the *coil* is a *short* and the *capacitor* is an *open*. At very *high* frequencies, the *coil* is an _____ and the *capacitor* is a _____ .

*

— — — — — — — — — — — — — —

open

short

5-121. Impedance coupling is *limited* to the high audio and low radio frequencies. Outside of these limits, the signal is either _____ or _____ .

*

— — — — — — — — — — — — — —

blocked

shorted

5-122. Here is an illustration of *transformer* coupling.

The output of Q_1 is developed across the _____ of T_1 and is _____ _____ coupled to the _____ .

*

— — — — — — — — — — — — — — —

primary

electromagnetically

secondary

5-123. The *primary* of T_1 is the _____ impedance for Q_1. The *secondary* is the _____ impedance for Q_2.

*

— — — — — — — — — — — — — — —

output (load)

input (base)

5-124. Since transformers come in a *wide variety*, this type of coupling can be used from *high audio frequencies to very high radio frequencies*. As frequencies increase, the iron core gives way to powdered iron, and finally, to air. Transformers used for coupling audio frequencies have an _____ core. The high radio frequencies use transformers with _____ cores.

*

— — — — — — — — — — — — — — —

iron

air

5-125. A valuable characteristic of the transformer for coupling purposes is its *ability* to match widely separated impedances. Almost any impedances can be matched by bridging the gap with a transformer with the proper _____ _____.

*
___ ___ ___ ___ ___ ___ ___ ___ ___ ___ ___ ___

turns ratio

Link Coupling

5-126. This is not a different type of coupling; it is a special *application* of transformer coupling. The application is illustrated by this drawing.

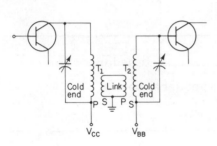

Actually there are two *widely separated* transformers with the output of one _____ to the input of the other.

*
___ ___ ___ ___ ___ ___ ___ ___ ___ ___ ___

linked

5-127. Tuned circuits are generally *unbalanced* so that one end has a higher signal potential than the other. The low signal end is called the *cold end*. In link coupling, best results are obtained by *linking* the cold ends of the two tuned circuits. The cold end of a tank circuit is the end of _____ signal potential.

*

— — — — — — — — — — — — — — — — —

lowest

5-128. One side of the link is generally *grounded* as shown in the illustration of frame 5-126. This *eliminates harmonics* and stray capacitance. Harmonics and stray capacitance can cause signal *distortion*. These can be eliminated in link coupling by _____ one side of the _____ .

*

— — — — — — — — — — — — — — — — —

grounding
link

FEEDBACK

5-129. The portion of the output signal which couples back to the input is *feedback*. Feedback is a common problem in transistors. If the feedback *aids* the incoming signal by being in phase with it, the feedback is *positive*. This is also called *regenerative* feedback. If the feedback *opposes* the incoming signal by being out of phase with it, the feedback is *negative*. Negative feedback is also called *degenerative* feedback. If a portion of the output signal couples back to the input and is *in phase* with the input signal, it is

_____ _____ .

*

— — — — — — — — — — — — — — — — —

regenerative (positive) feedback

5-130. If part of an output signal couples back to the input and is *out of phase* with the input signal, it is _____

_____ .

*

— — — — — — — — — — — — — —

degenerative (negative) feedback

5-131. *Positive* feedback _____ the input signal; *negative* feedback _____ the input signal.

*

— — — — — — — — — — — — — —

aids

opposes

5-132. Either positive or negative feedback can *cause problems* when it is not desired. *Neutralizing* circuits can be built to *eliminate* the effects of *undesirable* feedback. This is one type of neutralizing circuit.

A neutralizing circuit eliminates the effects of _____ _____ .

*

— — — — — — — — — — — — — —

undesirable feedback

5-133. Signal A (frame 5-132) is the *undesirable* feeback which couples back from collector to base. Signal B is the *feedback* which couples back through the *neutralizing* circuit. The effects of A will be *cancelled* by B because they are the same _____ and _____ degrees out of phase.
*

_____

amplitude
180

_____

5-134. When the components in the neutralizing circuit exactly *match* the internal impedance, the transistor feedback is completely *neutralized*. An effective _____ circuit must closely match the _____ impedance.
*

_____

nuetralizing
internal

AUDIO AMPLIFIER

_____

5-135. This amplifier is designed to amplify a *wide band* of frequencies which fall in the *audio* band of 16 Hz to 20 kHz. The audio amplifier handles a _____ _____ of _____ frequencies.
*

_____

wide band
audio

_____

5-136. Audio signals may be *very low* in amplitude and have *noise* frequencies mixed with them. The very low frequency audio signals need *special attention*. The audio amplifier circuit must contain a means of _____ noise, amplifying low amplitude signals, and showing special consideration for low _____ signals.
*

— — — — — — — — — — — — — —

reducing

frequency

5-137. *High fidelity* is a requirement for audio amplifiers. This means that the bias must be *stable*, and the operating point must be near the _____ __ ____ ____ portion of the curve.
*

— — — — — — — — — — — — — —

center of the linear

5-138. From previous information, the type of coupling is *likely* to be _____ .
*

— — — — — — — — — — — — — —

RC

5-139. This drawing shows *two audio* amplifier stages with RC coupling.

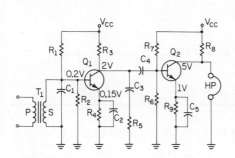

Maximum power is delivered to Q_1 by _____ coupling from the previous stage.

*
— — — — — — — — — — — —

transformer

5-140. C_1 *reduces* the noise level. This is possible because most of the noise is at relatively *high* frequencies. The capacitor offers a *high impedance* to the _____ frequencies and a low impedance to the _____ frequencies.
*
— — — — — — — — — — — —

audio

noise

5-141. Q_1 has a fixed bias on the *base* and a self-bias on the *emitter*. The self-bias aids the fixed bias and provides _____

_____ .

*
— — — — — — — — — — — —

thermal stabilization

5-142. C_3 and R_5 are a *shunting* network with an impedance inversely proportional to frequency. This forces the *low* frequencies to be *amplified* almost as much as the high frequencies. The shunting network enables nearly all frequencies in a wide band to receive _____ amplification.

*

— — — — — — — — — — — —

equal

5-143. C_4 and R_6 are *very large* components. A large capacitor offers *less* opposition to _____ frequency signals. A large resistor delivers maximum signal amplitude to the _____ resistance of Q_2.

*

— — — — — — — — — — — —

low

input

5-144.   The output of Q_2 is coupled to a pair of *headphones* by means of _____ coupling.

*

— — — — — — — — — — — —

direct

5-145. The *video amplifier* must be able to amplify frequencies from 0 to 4 MHz because the video signal is a *square wave* composed of *all these frequencies*. The video amplifier amplifies _____ waves which are composed of frequencies from _____ to ____ MHz.

*

— — — — — — — — — — — — — —

square

zero

4

5-146. These wave shapes illustrate the *composition* of a video signal.

Fundamental (1st harmonic)

3rd harmonic

5th harmonic

Combination

A *fundamental* frequency is also the *1st harmonic*. Harmonics are *multiples* of the fundamental frequency. Mixing the 1st, 3rd, and 5th harmonics produces the _____ wave shape.

*

— — — — — — — — — — — — — —

combination

5-147. This combination wave shape is *exaggerated*. Many harmonics are required to produce this much of a square wave. A well-shaped square wave consists of a *fundamental frequency and an infinite number of odd harmonics*. A video signal contains a _____ frequency and many _____ harmonics.

*

― ― ― ― ― ― ― ― ― ― ― ― ― ― ― ―

fundamental

odd

_____

5-148. *High* frequencies compose the *leading edge* of the video signal, and the *trailing edge* is made up of *low frequencies*. When *low* frequencies are not well amplified, the video signal is distorted on the _____ edge. Failure to properly amplify the *high* frequencies results in distortion of the _____ edge.

*

― ― ― ― ― ― ― ― ― ― ― ― ― ― ― ―

trailing

leading

_____

5-149. With a video signal, the frequencies of the *harmonics* which compose the signal are more important than the number of video signals that occur in a unit of time. Failure to amplify any of these harmonics will cause signal _____.

*

― ― ― ― ― ― ― ― ― ― ― ― ― ― ― ―

distortion

5-150. This is a *video amplifier* without the ordinary biasing circuits.

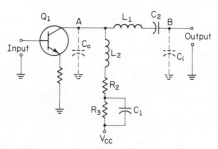

Broken lines indicate *distributive* capacitance. C_o is the output capacitance of the next stage. These capacitors *do not* exist at the low frequencies, but they become more and more prominent as frequencies _____ .

*

increase

5-151. R_1 is a *degenerative* feedback component. The potential across it always _____ the input signal.

*

opposes

5-152. The small amount of degeneration caused by R_1 *increases fidelity*, *broadens* the frequency response curve, and provides *thermal stabilization*. If R_1 had a capacitor across it, it would still give stabilized bias, but there would be no _____ _____ .

*

degenerative feedback

5-153. R_3 and C_1 form a *high* impedance to provide *maximum amplification for low frequencies*. L_1 counters the reactance of C_2 and *provides maximum coupling for low frequencies*. Both maximum _____ and maximum _____ are provided for _____ frequencies.

*

— — — — — — — — — — — — — — —

amplification

coupling

low

5-154. As the frequencies go *higher*, L_2 begins to form a *tuned tank* with the distributive capacitance. At *very high* frequencies, this combination becomes a *wide band, low Q, parallel resonant circuit*. This provides maximum gain and maximum coupling for the high frequencies. Both amplification and coupling of _____ frequencies are improved by the _____ resonant circuit. This tank is formed from the distributive capacitance in parallel with _____ .

*

— — — — — — — — — — — — — — —

high

parallel

L_2

5-155. If distortion still exists, variable resistors *can be* placed in *parallel* with the inductors. Varying these resistors will *change the Q* of the circuit which should tune out all distortion. Variable resistors in parallel with the coils can be varied to improve the _____ .

*

— — — — — — — — — — — — — — —

fidelty

5-156. A *driver* is a power amplifier which provides power to send a signal through a long transmission line, operate a speaker, drive an antenna, or trigger several circuits at the same time. Drivers are needed at *all* frequencies. A power amplifier which provides power for some special job is generally called a _____ .
Drivers are used at all _____ .

*

driver

frequencies

5-157. One type of driver is a *push-pull amplifier*. This drawing illustrates the basic circuit.

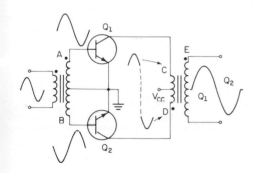

The two transistors conduct *alternately*. (All wave shapes are voltages.) Each transistor amplifies a different _____ of the input signal.

*

alternation

5-158. The input signals are fed to the base of the transistors from *opposite* ends of the transformer. This places the inputs _____ degrees out of phase.

*

180

5-159.   The *positive* to Q_1 causes it to *conduct* while the *negative* to Q_2 *cuts it off*.   On the next alternation, Q_1 is *cut off* by a _____ , and Q_2 is made to conduct by a positive.

*

— — — — — — — — — — — — — — — —

negative

5-160.   The *output* of each transistor is a _____ alternation of the amplified input, but they occur at different times.

*

— — — — — — — — — — — — — — — —

negative

5-161.   The output transformer *inverts* the output of ____ and makes it positive.   The output of ____ remains as a _____ .

*

— — — — — — — — — — — — — — — —

Q_1
Q_2
negative

5-162.   The *total output* of the transformer is a complete sine wave. Its positive alternation was amplified by ____ , and its negative alternation was amplified by ____ .

*

— — — — — — — — — — — — — — — —

Q_1
Q_2

5-163.   The *combined* dynamic transfer characteristic curves for the two transistors look like this.

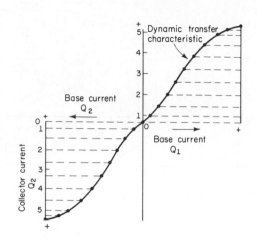

Both collector currents and base currents are in _____ directions.

*

— — — — — — — — — — — — — — —

opposite

5-164.   From previous information, operation on the *nonlinear* portion of the curve causes _____ .

*

— — — — — — — — — — — — — — —

distortion

5-165.   At the *cross over* point, both curves are *nonlinear*.   The
resulting distortion is illustrated here.

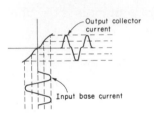

Both transistors have zero bias.   This places
the operating point in the area of maximum
_____ .

*

— — — — — — — — — — — —

distortion

5-166.   The push-pull amplifier operated at *zero bias* is a very
_____ fidelity circuit.

*

— — — — — — — — — — — —

low

Improving Fidelity

5-167.   *High fidelity* is essential to a driver.   The distortion
must be eliminated.   This can be done by *overlapping* the conduction
time of the two transistors.   With the proper overlap, curve A can
be changed to curve B.

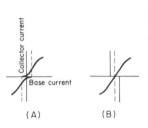

(A)   (B)

Adding a little *forward bias* will give the proper
_____ in conduction time.

*

— — — — — — — — — — — —

overlap

5-168. This is an improved circuit.

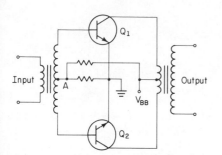

B+ and the voltage divider provide a
_____ potential at point A which
constitutes _____ bias for both
transistors.

*

- - - - - - - - - - - - - - - -

positive
forward

5-169. Now one transistor will be gradually cutting off while the
other is gradually increasing _____ .
*

- - - - - - - - - - - - - - - -

conduction

5-170. This drawing illustrates the operation of the amplifier in
frame 5-168.

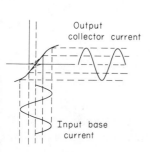

This shows maximum gain of both current and power
as well as a high degree of _____ .

- - - - - - - - - - - - - - - -

fidelity

SUMMARY

1. *Amplification* is the process of increasing the *magnitude* of a signal.

2. Amplifiers are called *voltage, current,* or *power* amplifiers according to the signal component they concentrate on.

3. When an NPN transistor is *properly* biased, the *emitter is negative* and *collector is positive with respect to the base.*

4. The *ratio* of output signal to input signal is *gain.*

5. *Class A* amplifiers conduct 100% of the time, B--50%, AB--more than 50% but less than 100%, and *C--less than 50%.*

6. A *signal* is wave variation with respect to time.

7. A transistor amplifier may be a *common base,* a *common emitter,* or a *common collector* configuration.

8. The *common base* produces amplification of voltage and power.

9. The *common collector* produces amplification of current and power.

10. The *common emitter* amplifies current, voltage, and power.

11. α represents maximum *current gain* in a common base amplifier, and $\alpha = \Delta I_c / \Delta I_e$.

12. β represents maximum *current gain* in the common emitter, and $\beta = \Delta I_c / \Delta I_b$.

13. *Static characteristic curves* are furnished by the manufacturer for the common base and common emitter.

14. A *load line* is a line connecting the points of maximum collector voltage and maximum collector current for a particular load resistor and collector supply voltage. It shows *all the possible relationships* of currents and voltages for a particular circuit.

15. The *bias* establishes the *operating point* on the load line, and the input signal causes a swing in both directions from this point.

16. The *constant power curve* is a line on the static characteristic curve chart which connects all points where current times voltage is equal to the rated power.

17. *Maximum safe power* gain is acquired when the load line is *tangent* to the constant power curve.

18. Projecting the values of I_b and I_c onto a separate chart generates the *dynamic characteristic transfer chart*.

19. *To avoid distortion*, operation must be on the most linear portion of the curve.

20. An *overdriven* amplifier may have distortion from both cut off and saturation *limiting*.

21. The *four* popular types of *coupling* are direct, RC, impedance, and transformer.

22. *Direct coupling* is suitable for dc, but its usefulness is limited by thermal instability.

23. *Transformer coupling* is the most flexible and can be used to match wide variations in impedances.

24. *Feedback* is the portion of an output signal which couples back to the input.

25. *Positive feedback* aids the input signal; *negative feedback* opposes it.

26. *Audio amplifiers* should be wide band, high fidelity amplifiers.

27. *Video frequencies* range from 0 to 4 MHz. A square wave is a video signal which contains *harmonics* over this entire range.

28. *Low frequencies* compose the *trailing edge* of a video signal; the *leading edge* is made up of *high frequencies*.

29. A *push-pull amplifier* is a type of *driver*. It should have maximum current and power amplification along with maximum fidelity.

30. *Forward bias* on both transistors eliminates *cross over* distortion in the push-pull amplifier.

SECTION 6
SIGNAL GENERATION AND CONTROL

A practical piece of electronic equipment contains a *variety* of circuits, and each type of circuit is designed to perform a *specific* task. Certain types of circuits appear over and over in nearly all types of equipment. In this section, we will examine some of the *frequently* used electronic circuits.

LIMITERS

6-1. A *limiter* is a circuit which controls the maximum amplitude of a signal. It is sometimes called a *clipper* because it clips off (eliminates) any part of the signal which exceeds the *specified limits*. A _____ controls the amplitude of a signal by _____ the undesired portion.

*

— — — — — — — — — — — — — — —

limiter
eliminating

6-2. We have *series* limiters and *parallel* limiters, and both of these
types have *both* positive and negative limiters. The *type* of limiter
is determined by how it is *connected* into the circuit. There are many
_____ of limiters and the type describes how it is _____ in
the circuit.
*

— ― — ― — ― — ― — ― — ― ― —

types
connected

Series Limiters

6-3. A *series* limiter can be designed to eliminate *all or part* of
either or both alternations of a signal. All series limiters have one
thing in *common*; the limiting device is in series with the signal
path. The *limiting device* is either a transistor or a diode. A
limiting device in series with the signal path is a _____ _____ ,
and it can be designed to eliminate _____ of the signal.
*

— ― — ― — ― — ― — ― — ― ― —

series limiter
any part

6-4. This is an *unbiased* series, positive limiter.

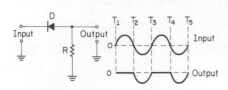

Each *positive* alternation reverse biases the diode and *cuts it off*. Each *negative* alternation forward biases the diode and causes it to drive *current* through the resistor. The positive alternations are _____, and the negative alternations are fully _____ and appear in the output.

*

— — — — — — — — — — — — —

eliminated

developed

6-5. The unbiased series, positive limiter *eliminates* the entire _____ alternation from each input sine wave.

*

— — — — — — — — — — — — —

positive

6-6. *Discrete parts* of the positive alternation can be eliminated by placing *forward bias* on the circuit in frame 6-4. Here we use 5 volts of bias.

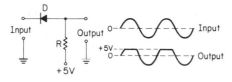

Now the diode will conduct as long as the input signal is *less than* 5 volts positive. The portion of the positive alternation which exceeds ___ volts is eliminated from the output. The remainder of the signal is _____ across the resistor.

*

— — — — — — — — — — — — —

5

developed

6-7. To eliminate *more than 50%* of a signal, *reverse bias* is used. This is the same circuit with 5 volts of reverse bias.

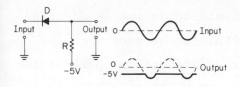

Now the diode conducts *only* when the input signal is *more negative* than the bias voltage. In this case, more than _____ percent of the signal is eliminated. Only the portion that is more than ___ volts negative will pass through the diode.

*

50

5

6-8. All limiters described thus far arc *positive* limiters. They can all be *changed* to negative limiters by *reversing the diode* in the circuit. Positive limiters eliminate the portion of a signal which exceeds the specified limits in a _____ direction. The direction of the diode determines if the limiter is _____ or _____ .

*

positive

positive

negative

Shunt Limiters

6-9. In the shunt limiter circuit, the limiting device is *parallel* to the signal path which means that the limiting is done when the device is *conducting*. The series limiter eliminates the part of the signal which occurs during ____ ____. The shunt limiter removes the part of the signal which occurs during _____ .

*

cut off

conduction

6-10. This is an *unbiased* shunt, positive limiter.

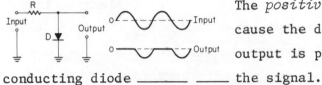

The *positive* alternations of the input cause the diode to conduct. Since the output is parallel to the diode, the conducting diode ____ ____ the signal.

*

shorts out

6-11. This diode in frame 6-10 has a *grounded* emitter. This means that it conducts any time the collector is *more positive* than _____ .

*

ground

6-12. Any portion of the signal *above zero* is shorted out by the diode. Since the *negative* alternation is *below zero*, it _____ ___ the diode and allows the signal to pass.

*

- - - - - - - - - - - - - - -

cuts off

6-13. *Less than 50%* limiting can be accomplished by using *reverse bias*, like this.

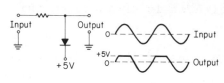

This diode will conduct *only* when the signal is *more than* ____ volts positive. The remainder of the time, the signal is allowed to pass.

*

- - - - - - - - - - - - - - -

5

6-14. *Forward bias* on the shunt limiter removes *more than 50%* of the signal as shown here.

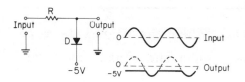

This diode will conduct and short out any part of the signal that is more _____ than a _____ ___ volts.

*

- - - - - - - - - - - - - - -

positive
negative 5

243

6-15. Any of the shunt positive limiters can be *changed* to negative limiters by *reversing the diode* in the circuit. The *negative* limiter removes any part of the signal that is more _____ than the specified limit.

*

— — — — — — — — — — — —

negative

6-16. The *double* diode limiter is used to eliminate a portion of of *both* alternations of the signal. The circuit is arranged in this fashion.

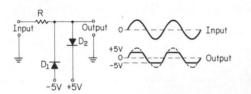

Without bias, one of the diodes would conduct on each _____ , and all of the signal would be _____ .

*

— — — — — — — — — — — —

alternation
eliminated

6-17. *With bias* as shown, D_2 conducts *only* when the signal is more than 5 volts _____ . D_1 conducts *only* when the signal is more than 5 volts _____ .

*

— — — — — — — — — — — —

positive
negative

244

6-18. When the signal is between _____ 5 volts and _____ 5 volts, *both* diodes are _____ and the signal is allowed to pass.
*

- - - - - - - - - - - - - -

positive

negative

cut off

6-19. Any device which acts as a *switch* can be used as a *limiting device*. *Transistors* can perform amplification along with _____ . An *overdriven* transistor can be both a _____ limiter and a _____ limiter.
*

- - - - - - - - - - - - - -

limiting

positive

negative

CLAMPERS

6-20. The *clamper* circuit establishes the *dc reference* for a signal. It is sometimes called a *dc restorer*. This circuit illustrates why clampers are *necessary*.

Capacitors are frequently used in this manner to block ____ and pass _____ .

*

- - - - - - - - - - - - - -

dc

ac (signals)

6-21. Without a signal, this capacitor has a five volt *charge* in the direction indicated. The charge may be any amount and in either direction. On the *positive* alternation of the signal, the capacitor charge is _____ to the signal amplitude. On the *negative* alternation of the signal, the capacitor charge is _____ from the signal amplitude.

*

— — — — — — — — — — — — — —

added

subtracted

6-22. *After passing* the capacitor, the ac signal will be riding a *dc reference* which is equivalent to the _____ on the _____ .

*

— — — — — — — — — — — — — —

charge

capacitor

6-23. At critical points in the circuits, *clamper stages* are installed to *fix the dc reference* to any desired level. Since references are *shifted* in both directions from zero, *both* positive and negative _____ are required.

*

— — — — — — — — — — — — —

clampers

6-24. A *positive* clamper establishes the dc starting point for a *positive going* signal. A *negative* clamper establishes the dc starting point for a _____ _____ signal.

*

— — — — — — — — — — — — — —

negative going

6-25. This is an *unbiased* positive clamper.

This circuit clamps the *bottom* of the positive going signal to a _____ potential.

*

zero

6-26. The capacitor has a *fast charge* path through the _____ and a *slow discharge* path through the _____ .

*

diode

resistor

6-27. Any part of the input signal that is *below zero* potential causes the diode to conduct and *charges* the capacitor as indicated. The charge on the capacitor becomes *equal and opposite* to the dc _____ that the signal is riding.

*

reference (potential)

6-28. The charge on the capacitor *exactly cancels* the dc reference potential of the incoming signal. In effect, the clamper *reshifted* the reference and clamped the bottom of the signal to _____ .

*

ground (zero)

6-29. The reference level established by the clamper can be fixed at any *desired* potential by placing *bias* on the diode. This is the result of *forward* bias.

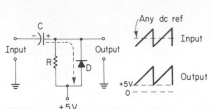

The diode retains a *charge* on the capacitor equal to the *bias* voltage when there is no signal. In this case, the capacitor is charged to ____ volts.

*

— — — — — — — — — — — —

5

6-30. In frame 6-29 any part of the incoming signal that is *less than* _____ volts will now cause the diode to conduct.

*

— — — — — — — — — — — —

positive 5

6-31. The dc reference potential of the incoming signal places an *additional charge* on the capacitor. The incoming reference potential is _____ , and the bottom of the output is clamped to the _____ potential.

*

— — — — — — — — — — — —

cancelled

bias

6-32. This drawing illustrates the results of *reverse* bias.

The capacitor is charged in the *opposite* direction by current through the resistor. The diode now conducts only when the input is more _____ than the _____.

*

— — — — — — — — — — — — — —

negative

bias

6-33. The *bias level* becomes the *clamping potential* for the most _____ portion of signal.

*

— — — — — — — — — — — — — —

negative

6-34. We have discussed only *positive* clampers, but any of them can be *changed* to negative clampers by *reversing the diode* in the circuit. *Positive* clampers set the dc starting point for _____ _____ signals. The *negative* clamper must, therefore, set the dc starting potential for _____ _____ signals.

*

— — — — — — — — — — — — — —

positive going

negative going

6-35.   A circuit which generates a *sawtooth* wave shape is called a *sweep generator* because most sweep circuits use such a wave shape. Another name for it is *time base generator*.   A time base generator, or a sweep generator, is a circuit which generates _____ wave shapes.
*

— — — — — — — — — — — —

sawtooth

Free Running Sweep Generator

6-36.   This is the sweep generator in its *simplest* form.

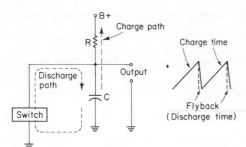

The circuit consists of an automatic *switching device* and an __ _____ .

*

— — — — — — — — — — — —

RC network

6-37.   When the switch is *open* in frame 6-36, the capacitor charges slowly through the _____ toward B+.
*

— — — — — — — — — — — —

resistor

6-39. The output is taken *across the capacitor*. It is a *sawtooth*-shaped voltage wave. The *rise time* is generated by the capacitor _____ and the *fall time* by the capacitor _____.

*

— — — — — — — — — — — — — — — — — — —

charge
discharge

6-40. The switch must be *voltage sensitive* so that it will auto-matically open to start the _____ time and automatically close to _____ it.

*

— — — — — — — — — — — — — — — — — —

sweep (rise)
stop

6-41. Rise time for the sweep needs to *linear*, but the capacitor charge is _____ .

*

— — — — — — — — — — — — — — — — — — —

exponential

6-42. More linearity is acquired by making the RC time constant *very large* and then using only about 10% of the possible capacitor charge. The *first 10%* of an exponential curve is very nearly a _____ _____ . As a sweep voltage, this part of the capacitor charge is almost _____ .

*

— — — — — — — — — — — — — — — — — — —

straight line
linear

6-43. In most cases, it is important that a sweep start at a
specific time. This is accomplished by *synchronizing* it with some
other signal. Here is one method of accomplishing this.

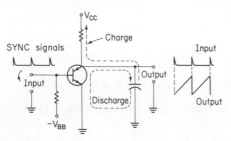

A *four layer* transistor is used as the
_____ _____ , and the output is
still taken across the _____ .

*

- - - - - - - - - - - - - - -

switching device
capacitor

6-44. At a certain *minimum* capacitor charge, the transistor *shuts
off* and starts a sweep. At a given *maximum* charge, the transistor
conducts and discharges the capacitor. When operated without an
input signal, the sweep generator is ____ _____ .
*

- - - - - - - - - - - - - - -

free running

6-45. The *synchronizing* signals *oppose* the bias and force conduction
to begin just before it would start anyway. Each signal then *causes*
the sweep that is in progress to _____ , and the next one starts
_____ .

*

- - - - - - - - - - - - - - -

terminate
automatically

6-46. Here is another means of synchronizing a sweep generator.

This is called a *gated* sweep generator. It uses a triode _____ as a switching device and has a _____ ____ input.

*

transistor
square wave

6-47. *Without an input,* this transistor conducts all the time and keeps the capacitor _____.

*

discharged

6-48. The *negative* alternation of the *input* wave shape holds the transistor ____ ____ and allows the capacitor to _____.

*

cut off
charge

6-49. The *positive* alternation of the *input* holds the transistor in a state of _____ . During this time, the capacitor _____ and remains in this condition.

*

— — — — — — — — — — — — — —

conduction
discharges

SQUARE WAVE GENERATOR

6-50. There are many ways to produce a square wave, but the most popular method is to use a *multivibrator*. The multivibrator circuit is designed *specifically* for the purpose of generating square waves. Square waves can be _____ in numerous ways, but the multivibrator is specifically designed as a _____ _____ generator.

*

— — — — — — — — — — — — — —

produced
square wave

6-51. This is a *free running* multivibrator.

This circuit produces a *series* of square waves at a frequency determined by its own circuit. It needs *no* input signal. The free running multivibrator determines its own _____ and produces a series of _____ .

*

— — — — — — — — — — — — — —

frequency
square waves

6-52. The *interconnection* of bases and collectors causes the transistors to *alternate* their conduction times. Since each triode is cut
off about *half* the time and conducting at saturation for the *other*
half, a square wave output can be taken from either point ___ or
point ___ .
*

A

C

6-53. When voltage is applied, one transistor goes to *saturation*
and holds the other *cut off*. This situation *reverses* periodically at
a rate determined by the *RC time constants* in the circuit. The transistors alternate between _____ and _____ at a rate
determined by the RC _____ _____ .
*

saturation

cut off

time constants

6-54. This chart shows the *wave shapes* for the circuit in frame 6-51.

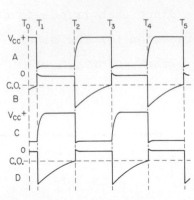

Wave shapes A, B, C, and D are taken from corresponding points in the circuit. Square waves appear at points A and ____ ; capacitor wave shapes appear at points B and ____ .

*

— — — — — — — — — — — —

C

D

6-55. The circuit is already in operation at T_0 with Q_2 *conducting* and Q_1 *cut off*. C_1 is *charging* through R_4 and R_1. C_2 is *discharging* through R_3 to ground. The discharge of C_2 is holding Q_1 cut off by keeping a _____ potential at point ____ .

*

— — — — — — — — — — — —

negative

B

256

6-56. At T_1, C_2 has *discharged* enough to allow Q_1 to conduct. The *current* through Q_1 causes its collector potential to drop to a *low* positive value. This forces C_1 to start *discharging* through R_4. The resulting negative potential at point D causes Q_2 *to cut off*. Point C rises to V_{CC} and causes C_2 to start *recharging* through R_3 and R_2. The rising potential at point B drives Q_1 into *saturation*. The *four* actions which occurred at T_1 are summarized by the wave shapes. Point A changed to a low positive potential; point B rose from negative to _____ , point C rose to a _____ positive, and point D dropped from zero to a strong negative.

*

_ _ _ _ _ _ _ _ _ _ _ _ _ _

zero

high

6-57. *From T_1 to T_2*, point A remains at a *low* positive potential because Q_1 is conducting at *saturation*. Point B remains at *zero* with C_2 fully *charged*. Point C remains at positive V_{CC} potential with *no current* through R_2. Point D grows progressively *less* negative as C_1 gradually *discharges* through R_4. Q_1 collector voltage is almost *zero* because Q_1 is _____ . Q_2 collector voltage is equal to V_{CC} because Q_2 is _____ _____ .

*

_ _ _ _ _ _ _ _ _ _ _ _ _ _

saturated

cut off

6-58. *At* T_2, C_1 has lost most of its *charge*, and the negative potential at point D is small enough to allow Q_1 to *conduct*. This
triggers a chain of events which results in Q_1 *cut off* and Q_2
saturated. *At* T_3, Q_1 goes to _____, and Q_2 _____ _____.
At T_4, Q_2 goes to _____, and Q_1 _____ _____.
*

— — — — — — — — — — — — — — —

saturation

cuts off

saturation

cuts off

6-59. If the circuit components are well *balanced*, each transistor
will *conduct half* the time and be cut off half the time. A continuous
chain of square waves may be taken from the _____ of either

_____ .

*

— — — — — — — — — — — — — — —

collector

transistor

6-60. The free running multivibrator can be *changed* to a synchronized
multivibrator by adding provisions for *input* signals, like this.

The input signal may be *either* a positive
or a negative. Since it is applied to the
base of *both* transistors, a *positive* will
trigger the *cut off* transistor into
_____ , or a *negative* will slow down
the conducting _____ . *Either* a
positive or a negative will cause a
_____ action.

*

- - - - - - - -

conduction

transistor

switching

6-61. *Each* subsequent signal will also cause a *switching* action.
Now the square waves are *started and stopped* by the _____
_____ signal.

*

- - - - - - - - - - -

synchronizing (input)

6-62. For *stable* operation, the synchronizing signal must be of a
frequency slightly *higher than twice* the free run frequency. In this
way, *each alternation* is forcefully switched just before it would
occur automatically. The wave shapes and circuit actions are the
same as before except for the _____ signal.

*

- - - - - - - - - -

synchronizing

6-63. With a slight change in the circuit, our synchronized multi-vibrator can be changed to this *bistable* multivibrator.

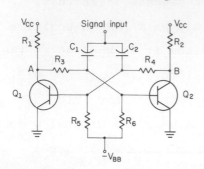

This circuit has *two* stable states. When either transistor is *cut off*, the other is *saturated*, and this state holds until an input signal *forces* a switching action. This circuit will change states only when _____ .

*

– – – – – – – – – – – – –

triggered

6-64. The negative potential $(-V_{BB})$ *is not* reverse bias, and it *is not* essential to the operation. It is there to improve *stability* by making sure that *only one* transistor can conduct at a time. It also *speeds* the switching action when the circuit is triggered. The negative potential speeds _____ action and improves _____ , but the circuit will function without it.

*

– – – – – – – – – – – – –

switching
stability

6-65. The bistable multivibrator is triggered for *every* single switching action. This means that the triggering frequency is _____ the output frequency.

*

– – – – – – – – – – – – –

twice

6-66.   The bistable multivibrator is also known as a *flip flop* and as an *Eccles-Jordan multivibrator*.   These are the wave shapes from the circuit.

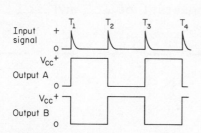

According to these wave shapes, the condition that existed *prior to* T_1 was Q_2 _____ ____ and Q_1 _____ .

*

_____ _____ _____ _____ _____ _____ _____ _____

cut off

saturated

6-67.   Another very useful circuit is the *monostable* multivibrator. It is a fairly simple circuit as shown here.

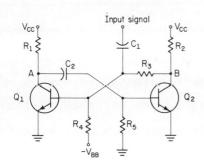

This circuit has *one* stable state: Q_1 cut off and Q_2 saturated.   A positive signal to the cut off base is necessary to *switch* the circuit out of this _____ _____ .

*

_____ _____ _____ _____ _____ _____ _____ _____

stable state

6-68. Once the trigger has *forced* the switching action, Q_1 saturates and Q_2 cuts off. This condition will continue as long as C_2 discharging through R_5 can *hold* Q_2 cut off. This is an *unstable* state, and its duration is determined by the time constant of ___ and ___ .
*

————————————————————————————————————

C_2
R_5

————————————————————————————————————

6-69. When C_2 has sufficiently discharged to *allow* Q_2 to conduct, the circuit *reverts* to its stable state with ___ saturated and _____ cut off.
*

————————————————————————————————————

Q_2

Q_1

————————————————————————————————————

6-70. The monostable multivibrator has been *dubbed a single shot* because one input trigger produces one complete output. It was at *one time* called a flip flop but that name has become attached to the bistable multivibrator by popular usage. The monostable multivibrator is also known as a _____ _____ .
*

————————————————————————————————————

single shot

6-71. Here are the *wave shapes* for the circuit in frame 6-67.

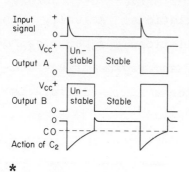

The frequency of the output is determined by the frequency of the _____ . The *duration* of the unstable state is determined by the discharge time of ___ .

*

— — — — — — — — — — — — —

input

C_2

OSCILLATORS

6-72. An *oscillator* is an electronic signal generator. Any *non-rotating* device which produces and maintains fluctuations at a pre-determined frequency is an oscillator. Under this broad definition, multivibrators are _____ .

*

— — — — — — — — — — — — —

oscillators

6-73. *Resonant circuits* will oscillate, but they require periodic injections of energy in order to *sustain* oscillations. Actually *four* elements are essential to sustained oscillations: a *power source*, *amplification*, a *frequency determining device*, and *regenerative feedback*. Any electronic circuit which contains these _____ elements is an _____ .

*

— — — — — — — — — — — — — — —

four
oscillator

Oscillating Crystals

6-74. A *crystal* will produce a voltage when subjected to a *mechanical stress* and it will produce mechanical *vibrations* when a *voltage is applied across it*. This is the *piezoelectric effect*. These mechanical vibrations occur at a highly *stable* frequency. This makes certain types of crystals valuable for frequency *control* of oscillators. Oscillators must contain a _____determining device. The piezoelectric effect of _____ enables their use for this purpose.

*

— — — — — — — — — — — — — — —

frequency
crystals

6-75. Crystals used in electronic circuits are *thin sheets* which have been cut from *natural* crystals. These sheets are ground to the *thickness* that produces the desired *frequency*. A thin sheet from a _____ _____ will oscillate at a frequency determined by its _____ .

*

— — — — — — — — — — — —

natural crystal

thickness

6-76. The crystal, combined with its holder, is a *resonant circuit* with a predetermined resonant *frequency*. The equivalent circuit is shown here.

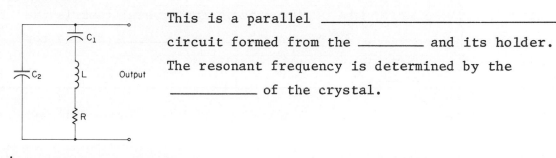

This is a parallel _____ circuit formed from the _____ and its holder. The resonant frequency is determined by the _____ of the crystal.

*

— — — — — — — — — — — —

resonant (tuned tank)

crystal

thickness

6-77. C_1, L, and R represent the electric *equivalent* of the vibrating crystal. C_2 is the capacitance between the metal plates of the
holder.   This is a *very effective* frequency determining device because
the crystal oscillates at a _____ _____ frequency.
*

_ _ _ _ _ _ _ _ _ _ _ _

highly stable

Crystal Controlled Oscillator

6-78.   This is a schematic of a *crystal controlled* oscillator.
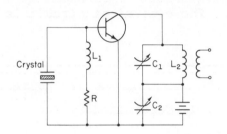
The symbol used for the crystal repre-
sents the *tuned tank* circuit previously
described.   The crystal tank is the
_____ _____ device for
this oscillator.

*

_ _ _ _ _ _ _ _ _ _ _ _

frequency determining

6-79. L_1 and R is a *self-biasing* network which also provides a discharge path for the crystal holder capacitor.   The transistor is an
_____ triode connected as a common _____ amplifier.
*

_ _ _ _ _ _ _ _ _ _ _ _

NPN
emitter

6-80. The collector *tank* circuit is tuned to the crystal *resonant* frequency. This tank is composed of ____ and ____.

*

— — — — — — — — — — — — —

C_1

L_2

6-81. There are *two* paths for regenerative *feedback*. One is through C_2, and the other is internal from _____ to ____.

*

— — — — — — — — — — — — —

collector

base

6-82. Application of voltage causes a *surge* of current through the crystal and starts oscillations. These oscillations are *signals* on the base of the transistor. The transistor amplifies each signal and *sustains* oscillations in the collector tank. *Feedback* from the tank circuit sustains oscillations in the crystal. The greatly amplified signal at the _____ frequency is _____ coupled to the next stage.

*

— — — — — — — — — — — — —

crystal

transformer

6-83. What is the frequency of the output? Pick one. It can be almost *any* frequency. *Fundamental* crystal frequencies range from 50 kHz to several MHz, and the oscillator *is not* limited to the fundamental frequency. Crystals produce usable frequencies up to the *seventh* harmonic. Crystal oscillators can be used for almost any _____ . The fundamental frequency of crystals coupled with the _____usable harmonics provide a very wide selection of oscillator frequencies.

*

— — — — — — — — — — — — — —

frequency

seven

Magnetostriction

6-84. The *magnetostrictive* effect of iron somewhat *resembles* the piezoelectric effect of crystals. When an iron rod is subjected to a rapidly *changing magnetic field*, the rod will change its *physical dimensions* in harmony with the changing field. The rod alternately *stretches and relaxes* as the flux expands and decays. This effect can also be used to control the frequency of an oscillator. The _____ effect of iron can be used to control oscillator _____ . This effect is apparent in the changing _____ of an iron rod in a rapidly changing magnetic field.

*

— — — — — — — — — — — — — —

magnetostrictive

frequencies

dimensions

6-85. When the changing field *matches* the resonant frequency of the rod, the iron will *vibrate* like a tuning fork. Iron may be *alloyed* with other materials to *improve* stability and enhance the magnetostrictive effect. All objects have *resonant* frequencies, and when a changing field matches the natural frequency of an iron rod in that field, the iron will _____ at its _____ frequency.

*

— — — — — — — — — — — — — — — — —

vibrate

resonant

6-86. This is a magnetostriction oscillator.

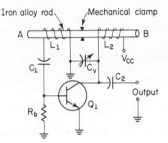

The iron rod with the coil arrangement is a magnetostriction *resonator*. It is often used as a _____ _____ device in audio oscillators.

*

— — — — — — — — — — — — — — — — —

frequency determining

6-87. The *first* fluctuation in collector current, even a slight *noise pulse*, will start a *shock wave* in the iron rod. The trigger is provided by any _____ in collector current, and it starts a _____ in the iron rod.

*

— — — — — — — — — — — — — — — — —

fluctuation

shock wave

6-88. The shock wave *travels* to point A, *elongating* the rod as it moves. The *movement* of the iron *creates a signal* in L_1 which goes back to the base and *causes another surge* of collector current. The shock wave is *reflected* from A back toward B and is *reinforced* by the second surge of collector current. The shock wave runs *back and forth* along the rod generating signals in both coils and being sustained by the surges of current through the transistor. The shock wave constitutes _____ , and the frequency is the natural frequency of the _____ .

*

— — — — — — — — — — — — — — — — —

oscillations
iron rod

6-89. C_r is a *tuning* capacitor which adjusts *both* coils to the resonant frequency of the rod. The output is coupled through C_2 as a *continuous* sine wave. This is an audio frequency, sinusoidal oscillator, and the frequency is determined by a _____

_____ .

*

— — — — — — — — — — — — — — — — —

magnetostrictive resonator

6-90.   This audio oscillator uses a *tuned tank* circuit to control
the frequency.

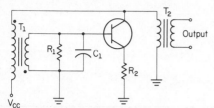

Feedback and output are transformer coupled.
At *audio* frequencies, these transformers
have _____ cores.

*

──── ── ── ── ── ── ── ── ── ── ──

iron

6-91.   The frequency determining tank circuit is the *secondary* of
_____ .   This transformer also provides _____ feedback.
*

──── ── ── ── ── ── ── ── ── ── ──

T_1

regenerative

6-92.   The tank circuit is *tuned* to the desired frequency by adjusting
C_1. R_1 is a *swamping* resistor.   It *limits* the feedback amplitude to
prevent *overdriving* the transistor. C_1 adjusts the _____ , and
R_1 adjusts the _____ .
*

──── ── ── ── ── ── ── ── ── ── ──

frequency
amplitude

6-93. R_2 provides *self bias*, and since it has *no* bypass capacitor,
it will cause some _____ and improve thermal _____ .
*

- -

degeneration
stability

Lag Line Oscillator

6-94. Any amplifier which has *sufficient* regenerative feedback will
become an oscillator because the other ingredients are present. This
is a *lag line* oscillator.

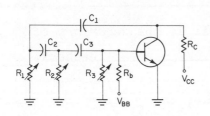

Since there *are no* crystals, coils, rods,
or tank circuits, both feedback and frequency
control must be accomplished by the _____
network.

*

- -

RC

6-95. This network is composed of *three* sections: C_1R_1, C_2R_2, and
_____ .
*

- -

C_3R_3

6-96. The remainder of the circuit is an *ordinary* common base amplifier with fixed _____ bias on the input.
*

— — — — — — — — — — — — — — — — —

forward

6-97. Each RC section must provide a 60° phase shift if the feedback is to be in phase or, at least, the total shift must be *180°*. Oscillation is started by a *stray noise* pulse which could be a lot of frequencies. *Some frequency* in the pulse will be shifted 180° and *reinforce* itself. If this *is not* the desired frequency, another can be *selected* by adjusting one of the resistors. The properly adjusted network provides _____ degrees of phase shift for the _____ frequency.
*

— — — — — — — — — — — — — — — — —

180
desired

Blocking Oscillator

6-98. This is a *blocking* oscillator.

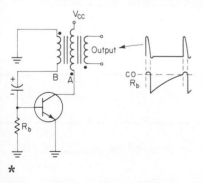

The name comes from the fact that conduction is *blocked* most of the time. The amplifier operates class ___, and the output is a string of _____ .
*

— — — — — — — — — — — — — — — — —

C
pulses

6-99. When I_c starts, point A goes *negative* and couples a _____ to point B.

*

positive

6-100. The *positive* at B causes current from ground to charge C in the direction indicated. This *current* develops a positive potential across R_b and drives the transistor into _____ .

*

saturation

6-101. A *steady* I_c stops the feedback. The *decaying* field on the secondary makes point B negative. Both coil and capacitor drive current *downward* through R_b. The resulting _____ on the base cuts off the transistor.

*

negative

6-102. The transistor will remain cut off until *both* coil and capacitor are fully _____ .

*

discharged

6-103. During each brief *conduction* period, a positive _____ is coupled across the transformer to the output.

*

pulse

6-104. This is a *synchronized* blocking oscillator.

This is identical to the previous circuit with the *exception* of the _____ and the _____ bias on the base.

*

- - - - - - - - - - - - - - -

input
reverse

6-105. The *reverse bias* blocks conduction until it is *triggered* by a positive input signal. Once triggered the circuit automatically builds to _____ then automatically _____ .
*

- - - - - - - - - - - - - - -

saturation
cuts off

6-106. One *output* will be produced for each _____ pulse.
*

- - - - - - - - - - - - - - -

input

6-107. Counting, multiplying, and dividing are some of the *arithmetic* performed on signal frequencies. If a frequency is *too low*, it can be ——————— ; if it is *too high*, it can be ——————— .
*

——— ——— ——— ——— ——— ——— ——— ——— ——— ———

multiplied
divided

Frequency Multiplier

6-108. This is a *frequency multiplier*.

It appears to be a basic ——————— .

*

——— ——— ——— ——— ——— ——— ——— ——— ——— ———

oscillator

6-109. It is a basic oscillator, but it *does not* oscillate at the input frequency. T_1 is tuned to the input frequency, and T_2 is tuned to *some multiple* of the input frequency. If it is to be a *frequency doubler*, T_2 is _____ the input frequency. If it is to be a *tripler*, T_2 is tuned to the _____ harmonic of the input.
*

---

twice
third

6-110. The *feedback* from the secondary of T_2 reaches the input in a manner to *reinforce* the proper harmonic of the incoming frequency. The operation is that of an oscillator, but the operating frequency is a _____ of the input.
*

---

multiple

6-111. Frequency doublers and triplers of this type are common. A *quadrupler* appears occasionally but a quadrupler has *too many circuit losses*. *Two doublers* give better performance than a *single quadrupler*. Quadruplers are scarce because of their excessive circuit _____.
*

---

losses

6-112. The bistable multivibrator is a *frequency divider*. It requires *two* signals in to produce *one out*. The input frequency is divided by _____ .

*

---

two

6-113. All types of *counters* produce an output after a specified number of inputs. All counters are _____ _____ .

*

---

frequency dividers

6-114. This is a schematic of a *frequency divider*.

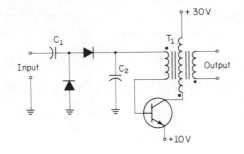

This is a combination of two simple circuits. The diodes and capacitors provide a *step-charging* action, and the remainder of the circuit is a _____ oscillator.

*

---

blocking

6-115. The 10 volts *reverse bias* holds the transistor cut off until
the charge on C_2 exceeds _____ volts.
*

— — — — — — — — — — — —

10

6-116. The *step-charging* circuit raises the charge on C_2 a small
amount with each input signal. After a specified number of inputs,
the charge on C_2 will *overcome the bias* and _____ the transistor.
*

— — — — — — — — — — — —

trigger

6-117. The blocking oscillator puts out *one pulse*, cuts itself off,
and waits for C_2 to _____ .
*

— — — — — — — — — — — —

recharge

6-118. These are the *wave shapes* for the circuit in frame 6-114.

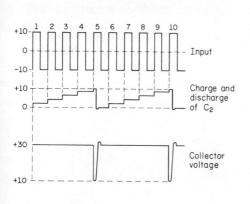

Every *fifth* positive input *triggers*
the oscillator and produces *one* output
pulse. This circuit is *dividing* the
input frequency by _____ .

*

— — — — — — — — — — — —

five

6-119. Frequency dividers are often called *counters* because they produce an output after a specified number of _____.

*

— — — — — — — — — — — — — —

inputs

6-120. The *accuracy* of a frequency divider depends upon inputs that are of a *constant amplitude, duration, and frequency*. The inputs are usually carefully *shaped* by wave-shaping circuits before they reach the divider. *Improperly* shaped waves at the input will produce an improper _____ at the _____.

*

— — — — — — — — — — — — — —

frequency
output

MODULATION

6-121. *Modulation* is a process of impressing intelligence upon a carrier frequency. The *three* popular types are *continuous wave, amplitude, and frequency*. Frequency _____ is one method of impressing a carrier wave with intelligence. There are _____ other popular methods.

*

— — — — — — — — — — — — — —

modulation
two

6-122. *CW modulation* is accomplished by *keying* the carrier wave on and off. This circuit shows one method of CW modulation.

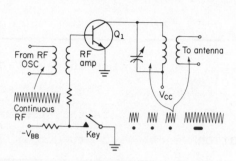

This RF amplifier is the last stage in the transmitter. Opening and closing the key turn the transistor _____ and _____ .

*

—— —— —— —— —— —— —— —— —— —— —— —— ——

on
off

6-123. *Continuous* RF is fed to the amplifier base, but if the key is *open*, fixed _____ bias blocks conduction.

*

—— —— —— —— —— —— —— —— —— —— —— —— ——

reverse

6-124. Each time the key is *closed*, a burst of RF oscillations will be amplified and passed on to the _____ .

*

—— —— —— —— —— —— —— —— —— —— —— —— ——

antenna

6-125. The circuit shows an output that *has been keyed* for the letter V in the international Morse code. The *length* of each burst of RF is determined by the length of time the key is _____. The *spacing* is determined by the length of time the key is _____.

*

— — —   — —   — — —   — —   — — —   — —   — — —   — —   — — —   — —   — — —   — —

closed

open

Amplitude Modulation

6-126. *Amplitude modulation* impresses the intelligence into the amplitude of the carrier. The RF carrier is *modulated* by an audio signal which causes the carrier *amplitude* to vary at the *audio* frequency. Amplitude modulation impresses an audio _____ into the _____ of a RF carrier.

*

— — —   — —   — — —   — —   — — —   — —   — — —   — —   — — —   — —   — — —   — —   — —

frequency

amplitude

6-127. *Sound waves* are changed to electric audio frequency waves by a *microphone* as illustrated here.

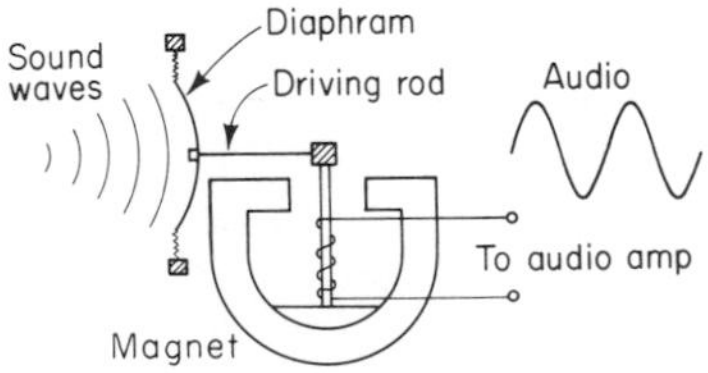

The sound waves cause a mechanical oscillation of the *diaphram* which duplicates the _____ of the sound waves.

Sound waves — Diaphram — Driving rod — Audio — To audio amp — Magnet

*

— — —   — —   — — —   — —   — — —   — —   — — —   — —   — —   — —   — — —   — —

frequency

6-128. The vibrating diaphram *varies* the armature. The vibrating coil *moves* in respect to the permanent magnetic field. The coil moving in the field has an ac _____ into it at the same frequency as the _____ waves.

*

─── ── ── ── ── ── ── ── ── ── ── ──

induced

sound

6-129. The *weak* audio signal can be used for modulation after it has been properly *amplified*. This block diagram illustrates the steps.

The modulator _____ the audio signal and uses it to control the gain of the RF _____ .

*

─── ── ── ── ── ── ── ── ── ── ── ──

amplifies

amplifier

6-130. The *RF oscillator* produces a _____ RF signal which is also applied to the RF amplifier.

*

─── ── ── ── ── ── ── ── ── ── ── ──

continuous

6-131. The RF signal goes into the *RF amplifier* with a constant amplitude and a constant frequency. The RF amplifier *does not* alter the frequency, but it will _____ the amplitude at an _____ rate.
*

—— —— —— —— —— —— —— —— —— —— —— ——

vary
audio

6-132. The *audio signal* varies the *bias* on the amplifier which changes its _____ at an audio rate. The resulting output is an RF carrier with the audio _____ impressed into its _____.
*

—— —— —— —— —— —— —— —— —— —— —— ——

gain
frequency
amplitude

Frequency Modulation (FM)

6-133. *Frequency modulation* impresses intelligence into the frequency of the carrier wave. The audio modulating signal causes the carrier frequency to *vary* at an audio rate. In frequency modulation, the carrier amplitude is held constant and the _____ is caused to vary at an _____ rate.
*

—— —— —— —— —— —— —— —— —— —— —— ——

frequency
audio

6-134. FM takes place at the *source* of the RF carrier as shown here. Q_1 is the *RF oscillator*, and Q_2 is the *modulator*. C_2 is the distributive capacitance between the _____ and _____ of Q_1.

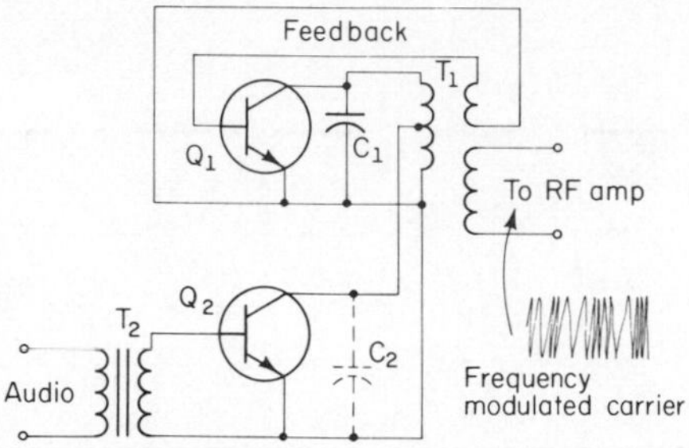

*

collector

emitter

6-135. C_2 is shown as a *variable* capacitor because it changes with the conduction of _____ .

*

Q_1

6-136. C_2 is also in *parallel with half* of the primary of T_1 which is the *tank circuit* for the oscillator. Therefore, when Q_2 changes conduction, the oscillator _____ _____.

*

changes frequency

6-137. The *conduction* of Q_2 is changing at an audio rate; the *center frequency* of the oscillator is changing at an _____ _____.

*

audio rate

6-138. The output of T_1 is a *constant amplitude* RF, but the audio intelligence has been *impressed* into its _____ .

*

— — — — — — — — — — — — — — —

frequency

DEMODULATION

6-139. *Demodulation* is the process of extracting the intelligence from a carrier wave. The carrier wave is the vehicle for *transporting* the intelligence. The modulator places intelligence on the _____ _____ , and it is removed by a process of _____ .

*

— — — — — — — — — — — — — — —

carrier wave
demodulation

6-140. Demodulation is done primarily through *heterodyning and detection*. Heterodyning is *mixing* two frequencies and extracting the difference. Detection is a combination of *rectification and filtering*. The intelligence can be extracted from a carrier wave by _____ and _____ .

*

— — — — — — — — — — — — — — —

heterodyning
detection

6-141. *Mixing* two frequencies and extracting the difference is _____ .

*

— — — — — — — — — — — — — — —

heterodyning

6-142. Rectification and filtering are _____.
*
— — — — — — — — — — — — — — — — — — —

detection

6-143. To the mixer, the *carrier wave* is one frequency and the other
is provided by an *RF oscillator* in the receiver. This oscillator
is called a *local oscillator*. It produces a *continuous* signal at a
predetermined frequency. One of the frequencies is the RF carrier
from the antenna. The other is produced by the _____ _____.
*
— — — — — — — — — — — — — — — — — — —

local oscillator

6-144. The *continuous* RF from the _____ _____ is mixed with
the incoming *modulated carrier* to produce a _____ frequency.
*
— — — — — — — — — — — — — — — — — — —

local oscillator
difference

6-145. This is a *mixer stage*. It mixes the two frequencies and extracts the difference frequency.

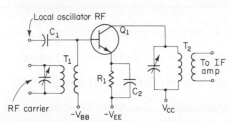

R$_1$ and C$_2$ form a *bias network* and provide _____ stabilization.

*

——— ——— ——— ——— ——— ——— ——— ——— ——— ——— ———

thermal

6-146. The *intermediate* frequency (IF) is the *difference* between the two incoming frequencies. Most communications and home entertainment receivers have an IF of 455 kHz. In this case, _____ kHz is the *difference* between the carrier and local oscillator _____ and, this is the frequency extracted by the _____.

*

——— ——— ——— ——— ——— ——— ——— ——— ——— ——— ———

455

frequency

mixer

6-147. The primary of T_2 is *tuned* to the IF. This means that, no matter what other frequencies are present, *only* the IF and a narrow band will be amplified by ____ and coupled out by ____ .
*

Q_1

T_2

6-148. There are *many* frequencies on the base of Q_1. We have the RF carrier, the RF from the local oscillator, the sum of these two, the difference, and many harmonics. The tuned primary of T_2 causes Q_1 to *select* from this maze the _____ _____ which becomes the IF.
*

---

difference frequency

6-149. The local oscillator is generally set to track 455 kHz *above* the incoming RF. *Moving the dial* to select a particular station tunes the first *RF stage* to that frequency and sets the *local oscillator* to 455 kHz above that frequency. When the receiver is receiving 1500 kHz, the RF amplifier is tuned to _____ kHz and the local oscillator to _____ kHz.
*

1500

1955

6-150. The frequency *response* of the tank in the collector of the mixer must be about 10 kHz for the proper reproduction of the intelligence. This is the *response curve* for that tank.

This shows a *band width* of ____ kHz and a *band pass* from ____ kHz to ____ kHz with the IF being the *center* of the band.

Gain

0.707

450   460
455

Frequency (kHz)

*

10
450
460

6-151. Leaving the mixer, we have a center frequency of _____ kHz and the intelligence has been *transferred* to the amplitude of this IF.

*

455

6-152. Sometimes the local oscillator and mixer are *combined* into a single stage. When this happens, the stage is called a *converter*. The converter is a single stage which does the job of both the _____ and _____ _____ .

*

mixer
local oscillator

6-153. The modulated IF must be *rectified and filtered* in order to extract the audio intelligence. This is a circuit used for that purpose.

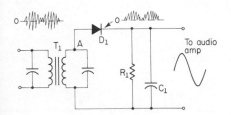

The modulated IF is coupled across T_1, and each time point A becomes _____ with respect to B the diode will conduct.

*

— — — — — — — — — — — —

positive

6-154. Any part of the incoming signal that is below *ground* level will cause the diode to _____ _____.
*

— — — — — — — — — — — —

cut off

6-155. Each *positive* variation develops a positive across R_1, and each *negative* variation is _____.
*

— — — — — — — — — — — —

eliminated

6-156. C_1 combined with R_1 *filters* out the IF component and leaves only the *audio envelope*. This envelope is a *duplicate* of the audio signal which originally modulated the ___ _____.
*

— — — — — — — — — — — —

RF carrier

6-157.   In FM, a *frequency discriminator* serves as a detector.   Here is the circuit of a frequency discriminator.

Its primary job is still _____ and _____ .

rectifying

filtering

6-158. L_1 and L_3 of the *three winding* transformer are tuned to the center frequency. C_c and L_2 are impedance coupling for the same frequency.   *Above* the center frequency, the coupling circuit is _____ .   *Below* the center frequency it is _____ .

*

inductive

capacitive

6-159.   The coupling impedance *varies* with frequency, and its output is *common* to the collector of both _____ .

*

diodes

6-160. The incoming IF is also *transformer coupled* to the
_____ of both _____ .
*

———— —— —— —— —— —— —— —— —— —— —— ——

collector
diodes

6-161. The diodes each have two voltages, and they conduct proportional to the *difference* between the two. D_1 conducts through
_____, and D_2 conducts through _____ .
*

———— —— —— —— —— —— —— —— —— —— —— ——

R_1

R_2

6-162. The voltage across *both* resistors is _____ with respect
to ground.
*

———— —— —— —— —— —— —— —— —— —— —— ——

positive

6-163. The output voltage *amplitude* is directly proportional to the
frequency of the IF. This varying frequency contains the intelligence.
When C_1 and C_2 filter out the IF components, they leave a *duplicate*
of the original _____ _____ .
*

———— —— —— —— —— —— —— —— —— —— —— ——

audio signal

SUMMARY

1. A *limiter* controls the maximum amplitude of a signal.

2. A series, positive limiter eliminates the part of a signal that is *more positive* than the specified limit.

3. The *shunt* limiter does its limiting when the diode is *conducting*.

4. *Bias* can be used on limiters to *set* the limit to any desired portion of the input signal.

5. A *clamper* circuit restores a signal to the proper *reference* level.

6. The positive clamper *fixes* the starting point for positive going signals.

7. The negative clamper *fixes* the starting point for negative going signals.

8. A simple *sweep generator* can be built with an RC network and a switching device.

9. In the sweep generator, the *charge voltage* on the capacitor is the *sweep voltage*. Only the first 10% of the capacitor charge is reasonably *linear*.

10. The *synchronized* sweep generator is *triggered* by the synchronizing signal.

11. The sweep voltage may be started and stopped on cue by *gating* the sweep generator.

12. A multivibrator is a *square wave* generator.

13. The *free run* multivibrator produces a chain of square waves at a frequency determined by its circuit components.

14. The free run multivibrator can be *synchronized* by applying either positive or negative signals to the base of *both* transistors.

15. The *bistable* multivibrator has *two* stable states, and every switching action must be triggered.

16. The *monostable* multivibrator has *one* stable state. When triggered, it goes to the unstable state for a period of time determined by its RC *time constant,* then automatically *reverts* to the stable state.

17. A *nonrotating* device which establishes and maintains fluctuations is an oscillator.

18. The *resonant frequency* of a crystal is determined by its *thickness*.

19. A crystal with its holder is equivalent to a *tuned tank* circuit.

20. The *magnetostrictive* effect of iron can be used to control oscillator frequencies.

21. A power source, amplification, regenerative feedback, and a frequency determining device are *all essential* to sustained oscillations.

22. In a *lag line* oscillator, the RC network *shifts* the feedback 180° for the frequency of oscillation.

23. The free run *blocking* oscillator generates a series of pulses.

24. The *frequency multiplier* is tuned to some *multiple* of the input frequency.

25. A *frequency divider* produces one output for a specified number of inputs.

26. *Modulation* is a process of impressing intelligence on a carrier wave.

27. *CW modulation* breaks the carrier into coded intervals.

28. *Amplitude modulation* impresses the intelligence into the carrier amplitude.

29. *Frequency modulation* impresses the intelligence into the frequency of the carrier.

30. The *microphone* changes sound waves to electric audio frequency signals.

31. *Demodulation* is a process of extracting intelligence from a modulated carrier wave.

32. The primary functions of demodulation are *heterodyning and detecting*.

33. *Heterodyning* is mixing two signals and extracting the difference.

34. *Detection* is rectification and filtering.

35. A *converter* performs as both a local oscillator and a mixer.

36. The *frequency discriminator* is an FM detector. It converts frequency variations into amplitude variations.

TRANSMISSION AND RECEPTION

Most of the receiver and transmitter circuits have been covered as separate items. Now we want to *assemble* them into *practical units* of electronic equipment. Since we have already examined the circuit details, we will use *block diagrams* while examining the structure of transmitters and receivers.

TRANSMITTER

7-1. A *transmitter* is that part of the electronic equipment which generates, modulates, amplifies, and radiates electromagnetic carrier waves. An *RF oscillator* which generates a carrier wave is part of a _____ .

*

— — — — — — — — — — — — — —

transmitter

7-2. Without describing all the functions of the transmitter, it could be called a device which *radiates intelligence* on *electro-magnetic waves*. A transmitter radiates _____ on _____ _____ waves.

*

— — — — — — — — — — — — — —

intelligence
electromagnetic

7-3. There are many *types* of transmitters, and the type identifies the *type of modulation* used. An *AM transmitter* uses ____ modulation. A *FM transmitter* uses ____ modulation.
*

—— —— —— —— —— —— —— —— —— —— —— ——

AM

FM

AM Transmitter

7-4. This is a block diagram of a *practical* AM transmitter.

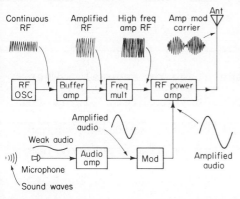

The *RF oscillator* may be crystal con-trolled or some other type of *stable* oscillator. It produces a _____ RF which will be used for the _____ _____ .
*

—— —— —— —— —— —— —— —— —— —— —— ——

continuous

carrier wave

7-5. Frequency *stability* is more important in the oscillator than the actual frequency it produces. The frequency can be _____ as many times as needed to raise it to the desired carrier frequency.
*

—— —— —— —— —— —— —— —— —— —— —— ——

multiplied

7-6. The *buffer amplifier* serves two purposes. It _____ the RF input and provides *isolation* (buffering) between the RF oscillator and frequency multiplier.

*

— — — — — — — — — — — — —

amplifies

7-7. The buffering action is necessary because any *stray* coupling or feedback between oscillator and multiplier will result in improper _____.

*

— — — — — — — — — — — — —

frequency

7-8. The *frequency multiplier* may be one stage or several. When used at all, it will be at least *one* frequency doubler. It is not rare to find a *doubler* followed by *two* triplers. This transmitter has a *center* carrier frequency of 1.5 MHz after the frequency has been multiplied by a doubler and two triplers. What is the frequency of the RF oscillator?

*

— — — — — — — — — — — — —

125 kHz

7-9. After the frequency multiplier, the carrier may go *directly* to the final RF power amplifier as shown in frame 7-4. However, in many cases, it is amplified through one or more *intermediate* amplifiers. The high frequency, high amplitude carrier is one input to the RF power amplifier. The other is an _____ signal from the _____ .

*

—   —   —   —   —   —   —   —   —   —   —   —   —   —   —

audio

modulator

7-10. The *audio* signal has been produced from _____ _____ entering the *microphone*.

*

—   —   —   —   —   —   —   —   —   —   —   —   —   —   —

sound waves

7-11. The weak audio signal from the microphone has been *amplified* through the _____ _____ and the _____ .

*

—   —   —   —   —   —   —   —   —   —   —   —   —   —   —

audio amplifier

modulator

7-12. The audio is applied to the RF power amplifier in a manner that it *varies the bias* on the transistor. The *gain* of the amplifier is then _____ proportional to the instantaneous amplitude of the _____ signal.

*

—   —   —   —   —   —   —   —   —   —   —   —   —   —   —

directly

audio

7-14. The varying gain *impresses* the audio signal into the *amplitude* of the carrier. This *complex* wave contains the center carrier frequency and *two side bands*. The *upper* side band is center RF plus audio; the *lower* side band is center RF minus audio. The *amplitude* of this complex signal is *varying* at the audio rate. This drawing illustrates the carrier content.

Upper side band
+
Center freq
+
Lower side band
} =
Modulated resultant

The amplitude-*modulated* carrier contains a center RF and two _____ _____ .

*
— — — — — — — — — — — — — —

side bands

7-15. The *upper* side band is _____ ___ frequency plus _____ frequency.
*
— — — — — — — — — — — — — —
center (RF)
audio

7-16. The *lower* side band is _____ frequency minus _____ frequency
*
— — — — — — — — — — — — — —

center
audio

7-17. With a center frequency of 1.2 MHz and an audio of 500 Hz, the *upper* side band is _____ kHz, and the *lower* side band is _____ kHz.
*
— — — — — — — — — — — — — —

1200.5
1199.5

300

7-18. We must keep in mind that the audio signal *is not a simple* stable frequency. It may be *varying* all over the audio band in order to directly represent every sound entering the microphone. A *fixed* audio signal could carry no intelligence. Therefore, the frequencies of the two side bands are *shifting* about with every change in the _____ frequency.

*

— — — — — — — — — — — — — —

audio

7-19. The *band width* is measured from the lowest to the highest side band frequency. This entire band must be transmitted from the antenna to avoid *loss* of intelligence. The band width is calculated as *twice* the highest frequency of the modulating wave. Suppose that our 500 Hz signal varies up to 750 Hz. The *band width* is then _____ kHz.

*

— — — — — — — — — — — — — —

1.5

7-20. The *band pass* is the center frequency of the carrier plus and minus 1/2 of the band width. From our previous figures, we have a *band pass* from _____ kHz to _____ kHz.

*

— — — — — — — — — — — — — —

1199.25
1200.75

7-21.   This drawing illustrates the side bands and how they are formed.

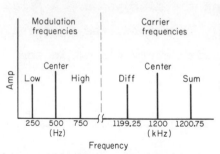

The tank circuit for the RF power amplifier should have a *center frequency* of _____ kHz and a *band pass* wide enough to include both ____ ____ .

*

- - - - - - - - - - - - - - - - - - -

1200

side bands

7-22.   This represents the *response curve* for the RF power amplifier tank circuit.

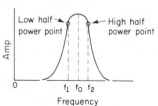

According to our previous figures, f_o should be _____kHz, f_1 must be *at least as low* as _____ kHz, and f_2 must be *at least as high* as _____ kHz.

*

- - - - - - - - - - - - - - - - - - -

1200

1199.25

1200.75

7-23. The *ratio* of the voltage amplitude of the modulation signal
to the voltage amplitude of the carrier wave is the *degree of modu-*
lation: $M = E_m/E_c$. The degree of modulation may be changed to
percent of modulation by multiplying by 100. M is always one or less;
therefore, percent of modulation can be a maximum of _____ percent.
*

— — — — — — — — — — — — — —

100

7-24. It is desirable to operate *near 100%* modulation because this
provides *maximum power* for the side bands. It is possible to *over*
modulate, and this will generate *undesirable* frequencies. 100%
modulation provides maximum power for the _____ _____ , but over
modulation creates _____ frequencies.
*

— — — — — — — — — — — — — —

side bands
undesirable

7-25. This drawing *illustrates* correct, over, and under modulation.

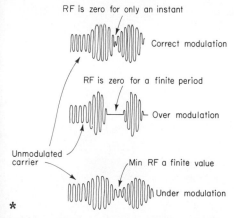

RF is zero for only an instant

Correct modulation

RF is zero for a finite period

Over modulation

Unmodulated
carrier

Min RF a finite value

Under modulation

The maximum amplitude of *correct* modulation is *twice* the amplitude of the
unmodulated carrier. The minimum
amplitude is _____ , but it should remain
at this amplitude for only an _____
of time.
*

— — — — — — — — — — — — — —

zero

instant

303

7-26.   The *under* modulated wave lacks sufficient *amplitude* and never reaches the proper _____ value.
*
__ __ __ __ __ __ __ __ __ __ __ __

minimum

7-27.   The *over* modulated wave reaches a maximum amplitude that is too _____ and remains at the minimum value for a _____ period of time.
*
__ __ __ __ __ __ __ __ __ __ __ __

high
finite

FM Transmitter

7-28.   The FM transmitter *impresses* the intelligence on the carrier wave by varying its _____ .
*
__ __ __ __ __ __ __ __ __ __ __ __

frequency

7-29.   This is a block diagram of a *practical* FM transmitter.

Amplified audio

Sound
Audio
Audio amp
Modulator
RF OSC

FM carrier
Amplified FM carrier
Correction freq

Buffer
Freq mult
Auto freq control

Multiplied frequencies of carrier

Driver
RF power amp

Frequency modulated carrier

The *RF oscillator* is tuned to a fixed frequency and, without out-side influence, will produce a *continuous* RF at a fixed fre-quency and a fixed amplitude. If the modulator input is removed, the RF oscillator produces a _____ frequency at a _____ amplitude.

*

fixed
fixed

7-30.   The oscillator frequency is *influenced* by the _____ signal from the _____ .

*

audio
modulator

7-31.   *Another signal* which may alter the oscillator is the correction signal which feeds back from the automatic _____ _____ circuit.

*

frequency control

7-32. The *automatic frequency control* (AFC) circuit has a reference frequency which represents the *correct* center frequency of the transmitter. Any *variation* from this standard creates a correction signal which changes the _____ _____ of the RF oscillator.
*

center frequency

7-33. The *audio signals* from the microphone are processed through a network that *does not* appear on the block diagram. It is called a *preemphasis* network, and it increases the amplitude of the *high* audio frequencies. Without this network, some of the high frequency audio signals would be *lost* in the circuit noise. The preemphasis network _____ the amplitude of _____ audio frequencies to prevent losing some of these signals in the circuit _____ .
*

increases

high

noise

7-34. The complex audio wave (varying with every fluctuation of sound) is amplified through *one or more* stages of broad band _____ _____ before reaching the modulator.
*

audio amplifiers

7-35. The *modulator* is the final audio amplifier, and its circuits are *interwoven* with those of the ____ _____ .
*

RF oscillator

7-36. The audio signals from the modulator *alter* the characteristics of the RF oscillator and cause a _____ variation in both directions from the _____ frequency.
*

— —— — —— — —— — —— — —— — —— — —— — —— — —— — ——

frequency

center

7-37. The center frequency is also known as the *rest frequency*, which simply means the *unmodulated* frequency. When no audio is present, the oscillator is producing the _____ or the _____ frequency.
*

— —— — —— — —— — —— — —— — —— — —— — —— — —— — ——

center

rest

7-38. A *low frequency* audio causes a *slow* change in oscillator frequency; a *high frequency* audio causes a *rapid* change. The rate of frequency change in the oscillator is _____ proportional to the audio frequency.
*

— —— — —— — —— — —— — —— — —— — —— — —— — —— — ——

directly

7-39. A *low amplitude* audio causes a *small shift* from the center
frequency; a *high amplitude* causes a *wide swing*. This is illustrated

The amplitude of the _____ signal determines

the _____ of frequency variation to

either side of _____ frequency.

Carrier frequency   (kHz)

*

— — — — — — — — — — — — — —

audio

amount (degree)

center

7-40. Both audio signals in frame 7-39 are of the *same* frequency,
but AF-2 changes the carrier frequency _____ as much as AF-1 because
its _____ is twice that of AF-1.

*

— — — — — — — — — — — — — —

twice

amplitude

7-41. This drawing illustrates the *modulating effect* of two cycles of audio which are different in both frequency and amplitude.

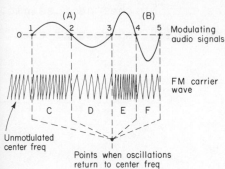

The carrier frequencies are compressed in areas C and E. The frequencies in area E are more compressed (higher frequencies) than those in area C. This effect is caused by the difference in _____ between waves A and B.

*

— — — — — — — — — — — — — — —

amplitude

7-42. Areas D and F are *rarefied* with lower frequencies in F than in D. This is also a result of the difference in _____ of waves A and B.

*

— — — — — — — — — — — — — — —

amplitude

7-43. Points 1, 2, 3, 4, and 5 represent the points where the carrier frequency returns to *center*. These points correspond to _____ _____ on the modulating wave.

*

— — — — — — — — — — — — — — —

zero amplitude

7-44. All the side bands are contained in the *frequency variations,* and these are more complex than they appear. There are a *great many* side bands and it is desirable to retain as many of them as possible. The frequency variations contain _____ side bands, and most of them should be _____ .
*

___ ___ ___ ___ ___ ___ ___ ___ ___ ___ ___ ___ ___

many

retained

7-45. The *first high* side band is center frequency plus audio frequency. The *first low* side band is center frequency minus audio frequency. *Successive high side bands* are obtained by successive addition of the audio frequency to the *last* side band frequency. *Successive low side bands* are obtained by successive subtraction of the audio frequency. With a *center* frequency of 100 kHz and an *audio* of 500 Hz the *first upper side band* frequency is _____ kHz, and the *first lower side band* frequency is _____ kHz.
*

___ ___ ___ ___ ___ ___ ___ ___ ___ ___ ___ ___ ___

100.5

99.5

7-46. At the same frequencies described in frame 7-45, the *second high* side band frequency is _____ kHz, and the *second low* side band is _____ kHz.
*

___ ___ ___ ___ ___ ___ ___ ___ ___ ___ ___ ___ ___

101

99

7-47. These side bands extend *on and on* in both directions as illustrated here.

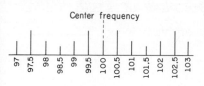

Center frequency

97 97.5 98 98.5 99 99.5 100 100.5 101 101.5 102 102.5 103

Frequencies (kHz)

As the *deviation* from the center frequency increases, the amplitude of the side bands _____ .

*
— — — — — — — — — — — — —

decreases

7-48. All *significant* side bands must be retained, and they are significant until their amplitude becomes *less than one percent* of the carrier amplitude. All side bands with amplitudes as much as _____ percent of the carrier amplitude are _____ side bands and must be retained.

*
— — — — — — — — — — — — —

one

significant

7-49. A *modulation index* (M) can be calculated by dividing the frequency deviation (f_d) of the carrier by the highest frequency (f_m) of the modulating signal: $M = f_d/f_m$. Where frequency deviation is 1000 Hz and audio is 500 Hz, the modulation index is _____ .

*
— — — — — — — — — — — — —

2

7-50. The modulation index leads us to a standard modulation *index table* similar to this.

Modulation index	Side bands	Band width
1	6	6 x A
2	8	8 x A
3	12	12 x A
4	14	14 x A
5	16	16 x A

This table indicates the *number* of significant _____ _____ for any given value of _____ _____ .

*
— — — — — — — — — — — — — — — —

side bands

modulation index

7-51. The table also provides data for calculating the *band width* by giving a number by which the audio frequency is to be multiplied. With our modulation index of 2, we have ____ significant side bands and a band width of ____ times 500 Hz.

*
— — — — — — — — — — — — — — — —

8

8

7-52. With an audio signal of 2 kHz and a modulation index of 5, we have ____ significant side bands and a band width of ____ kHz.

*
— — — — — — — — — — — — — — — —

16

32

7-53. *Wide band* FM has a frequency range of several hundred megahertz. It produces *high fidelity* because it retains nearly all significant side bands. *Narrow band* FM limits the number of side bands and suffers a *loss* in fidelity for the sake of having more channels in a given frequency spectrum. FM falls into *two* categories: band and   band.

*

wide

narrow

7-54. *Wide band* retains more   and produces higher

    .

*

side bands

fidelity

7-55. *Narrow band* sacrifices some   in order to concentrate more   into a given frequency spectrum.

*

fidelity

channels

7-56. Back to the block diagram, the complex FM carrier passes through a *buffer stage* which amplifies the carrier while providing isolation between the RF oscillator and the   .

*

frequency multiplier

7-57. Again the *frequency multiplier* may contain as many stages of multiplication as necessary. In most cases, *three* stages are sufficient. They generally consist of a frequency _____ and two triplers.

*

___ ___ ___ ___ ___ ___ ___ ___ ___ ___ ___ ___

doubler

7-58. When the RF oscillator *rest frequency* is 100 kHz with 500 Hz variations, the output of the multiplier is _____kHz with ___ kHz variations. (Assume that the multiplier consists of a doubler and two triplers.)

*

___ ___ ___ ___ ___ ___ ___ ___ ___ ___ ___ ___

1800

9

7-59. The *actual center frequency* of the multiplier output is constantly compared against the *ideal* center frequency in the automatic frequency control circuits. When the two frequencies *fail to match*, these circuits generate a _____ signal which changes the center frequency of the ____ _____ .

*

___ ___ ___ ___ ___ ___ ___ ___ ___ ___ ___ ___

correction

RF oscillator

7-60. The *driver* stage provides some amplification, but more important, it *isolates* the frequency multiplier from the RF _____ _____ .

*

— — — — — — — — — — — — — — — — —

power amplifier

7-61. The *RF power amplifier* provides sufficient power to radiate the signal from the antenna. The power amplifier must be a _____ _____ amplifier in order to handle the complex wave shape.

*

— — — — — — — — — — — — — — — — —

broad band

Single Side Band (SSB) Transmitter

7-62. The (SSB) transmitter is an *AM transmitter* which uses only *one* side band. This is accomplished by removing the _____ frequency and one of the _____ _____ .

*

— — — — — — — — — — — — — — — — —

carrier

side bands

7-63.   The single side band transmitter has *two* particularly useful features.   The narrow band enables a given transmitter to provide *more power per frequency* transmitted, and many *more channels* can be used in a given frequency spectrum.   The result is a _____ signal and some relief in the crowded frequency _____.

*

stronger

spectrum

7-64.   This is a block diagram of a *practical* single side band transmitter.

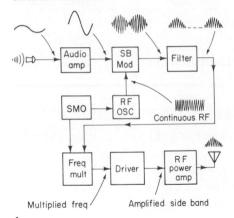

The SMO is an abbreviation for *stabilized master oscillator*, and it is one of the two completely new stages in this transmitter.   The other new stage is the

_____.

*

filter

7-65.   The modulator is called a *side band modulator* because its output essentially consists of the upper and lower _____ _____.

*

side bands

7-66. The modulator has *two inputs*: the audio signal and a
_____ RF from the RF oscillator.

*

continuous

7-67. The modulator is tuned to *suppress both* the audio and carrier
frequency, but it will amplify and pass *both the side bands*. The
modulator removes the basic _____ and _____ frequencies, but
passes the _____ and _____ of these two frequencies.

*

audio
carrier
sum
difference

7-68. The *two side bands* from the modulator pass into a *filter* with
a high Q tank circuit. A crystal is frequently used for this tank.
The filter passes a band of frequencies just wide enough to include
all frequencies of *only one side band*. The filter _____ the
selected side band and _____ all other frequencies.

*

passes
rejects

7-69. This drawing illustrates the *frequency response* curve of the filter.

f_r is the *center* frequency of the selected _____ _____ .

*

— — — — — — — — — — — — —

side band

7-70. The *sharp cut off* characteristics of the filter make sure that only the frequencies of the selected _____ _____ can pass.

*

— — — — — — — — — — — — —

side band

7-71. *Either side band* may be used since each side band contains all of the intelligence. The filter is tuned to select either the _____ or the _____ side band.

*

— — — — — — — — — — — — —

upper
lower

7-72. The method of frequency *multiplication* varies from one SSB
transmitter to another. One method is *heterodyning*. Since we are
raising the frequencies of our selected side band, if heterodyning
is used, we would extract the ＿＿＿ frequencies rather than the

＿＿＿＿＿＿ .

*

— — — — — — — — — — — — — —

sum

difference

7-73. The *remainder* of the stages from the multiplier to the antenna
are similar to those covered in previous transmitters. They are,
however, *narrow band* as compared to a standard AM transmitter. The
driver and power amplifier in a SSB transmitter are ＿＿＿＿ band which
enables a higher ＿＿＿＿＿＿ of the available power.

*

— — — — — — — — — — — — — —

narrow

concentration

7-74. The frequency of a SSB transmitter is very *critical*. A 50 Hz
variation in a 4 MHz signal is sufficient to cause noticeable *dis-*
tortion of the voice. This requires special considerations in the
area of ＿＿＿＿ stability.

*

— — — — — — — — — — — — — —

frequency

7-75. The *SMO* provides this stability. It works on a highly *stable* *frequency standard* on the order of 100 kHz. This is often provided by a crystal which is kept in a *constant temperature oven*. A crystal is one method of obtaining the highly _____ frequency standard required by the _____ .

*

— — — — — — — — — — — — — — —

stable

SMO

7-76. The SMO *forces* this frequency standard on the RF oscillator and the frequency multiplier by a synchronizing process known as *phase* *locking*. Phase locking synchronizes the _____ frequencies with the

_____ _____ .

*

— — — — — — — — — — — — — — —

higher

frequency standard

7-77. Frequency *corrections* are made the instant a signal at any point starts to get out of _____ with the frequency _____ .

*

— — — — — — — — — — — — — — —

phase

standard

RECEIVERS

7-78. *The receiver* is the portion of electronic equipment which plucks electromagnetic signals from space, amplifies them, extracts the intelligence, and reproduces the sound which entered the micro-phone in the transmitter. It could be said that a receiver _____ and decodes the information radiated by the _____ .
*

intercepts
transmitter

7-79. There is a *type* of receiver to match each type of transmitter, and the type specifies the type of _____ the receiver is equipped to handle.
*

modulation

AM Receiver

7-80. The AM receiver is designed to handle transmissions from the standard *AM transmitter*. Therefore, it is equipped to decode a standard _____ carrier.
*

amplitude-modulated

7-81. This is a block diagram of a *practical* AM receiver.

This receiver works with the *full band* of frequencies which means a _____ with _____ side bands.

*
_____

carrier

two

_____

7-82. Most AM receivers are of the *superheterodyne* type. This indicates that frequency _____ is part of the decoding process.

*
_____

mixing

_____

7-83. This receiver has a *local oscillator and a mixer*; therefore, it is a _____ receiver.

*
_____

superheterodyne

_____

7-84. The very weak, amplitude-*modulated carrier* is picked up on the antenna and sent into the RF amplifier. The *RF amplifier* is one or more stages placed strategically as near the antenna as possible. This provides amplification for the _____ incoming signals before they can become lost in the circuit noise.

*
_____

weak

_____

7-85. There is a great *variety* of frequencies on the antenna. The setting of the *channel selector* control determines which frequencies will be allowed to enter. Varying the selector control selects the _____ frequencies from among a great many _____ frequencies.

*

— — — — — — — — — — — — — —

desirable

undesirable

7-86. The selector control *tunes* the RF amplifier and mixer to the *center frequency* of the band selected and tunes the local oscillator 455 kHz above this frequency. The selector control tunes the _____ _____ , the _____ , and the _____ _____ .

*

— — — — — — — — — — — — — —

RF amplifier

mixer

local oscillator

7-87. When the selector control is set for receiving *1000 kHz*, the RF amplifier and mixer are tuned to _____ kHz and the local oscillator is tuned to _____ kHz.

*

— — — — — — — — — — — — — —

1000

1455

7-88. The difference between the received signal frequency and the local oscillator frequency is the *intermediate frequency* (IF). While 455 kHz is the most common IF, there is no rule that limits it to this frequency. Also, the local oscillator generally *tracks above* the selected frequency, but it *could be* set to track below the incoming frequency. The IF is the difference between the _____ _____ frequency and _____ frequency. A common IF is _____ kHz.

*

— — — — — — — — — — — — — — — —

signal (carrier)
local oscillator
455

7-89. After amplification, the *incoming* frequencies are coupled to the mixer. The *other input* to the mixer comes from the _____ _____ .

*

— — — — — — — — — — — — — — — —

local oscillator

7-90. The *local oscillator* is often crystal controlled because it needs to be tunable over a wide range and should be stable on any set frequency. The local oscillator must be _____ and _____ over a wide range of frequencies.

*

— — — — — — — — — — — — — — — —

tunable
stable

7-91. The *mixer* beats the two inputs together and *extracts* the difference frequency. The *band* of frequencies from the mixer should be about 10 kHz wide with the ____ kHz as the center frequency.

*

___ ___ ___ ___ ___ ___ ___ ___ ___ ___ ___

455

7-92. When the incoming signal *varies* from 955 kHz to 1005 kHz, the IF will vary from ____ kHz to ____ kHz.

*

___ ___ ___ ___ ___ ___ ___ ___ ___ ___ ___

450
460

7-93. The mixer output is a *complex* signal with frequencies varying around the 455 kHz center frequency. This signal is also *amplitude modulated* since the carrier modulation has been transferred to the

_____.

*

___ ___ ___ ___ ___ ___ ___ ___ ___ ___ ___

IF

7-94. The *IF amplifier* represents several stages of amplifiers. They are commonly referred to as the *IF strip*. These amplifiers are relatively narrow band, tuned transformer coupled, radio frequency amplifiers because the IF is actually a low frequency radio signal. The IF strip consists of several _____ of _____ amplifiers.

*

— — — — — — — — — — — — — —

stages
tuned

7-95. The output of the final IF amplifier is coupled to the *detector* as shown in our block diagram if the receiver uses single conversion. If *double conversion* is used, it goes to a *second mixer* to be mixed with the frequency from another local oscillator. A double conversion receiver has two _____ and two _____ _____.

*

— — — — — — — — — — — — — —

mixers
local oscillators

7-96. Double conversion is often used when the carrier frequency is on the order of *several megahertz*. The *first mixer* produces an IF that is still a fairly high radio frequency. The *second mixer* reduces the first IF to a *lower* frequency second IF. Double conversion is generally used with very _____ carrier frequencies. This frequency is reduced in two steps to reach the final ____ .
*

— — — — — — — — — — — — — —

high
IF

7-97. The *detector* extracts the intelligence from the modulation on the IF. This is accomplished by *two* actions: _____ and _____ .
*

— — — — — — — — — — — — — —

rectification
filtering

7-98. The *rectifier removes* half of each IF wave shape and the *filter removes* the IF components. This leaves the _____ signal which is a *duplicate* of the signal used for _____ in the transmitter.
*

— — — — — — — — — — — — — —

audio
modulation

7-99.   After amplification, the audio signal is used to *drive* a speaker and the speaker is made to *reproduce* the sound waves which entered the _____ of the transmitter.

*

microphone

7-100.   The *automatic gain control* (AGC) circuit compensates for both too weak and too strong signals by *changing the gain* of all amplifiers prior to the detector.   This is an automatic gain control circuit. The output of the detector contains a *dc component* which is directly proportional to the *average* amplitude of the signal. The AGC circuit uses this dc to control the gain of the IF strip, _____ , and _____ _____ .

*

mixer

RF amplifiers

7-101.   A signal *weaker than average* will be amplified _____ than average.   A signal that is *stronger than average* will receive _____ than average amplification.

*

more

less

7-102. This is a block diagram of a *practical* FM receiver.

It is designed to handle information radiated from a _____ _____ transmitter.

*

— — — — — — — — — — — —

frequency-modulated (FM)

7-103. Our FM receiver uses a *converter* which does the job of both _____ and _____ _____ .

*

— — — — — — — — — — — —

mixer
local oscillator

7-104. The oscillator section of the converter produces a frequency equal to the *center* frequency of the received carrier plus the IF. Incoming frequencies mix with the locally produced frequency and the *IF is extracted*. The frequency modulation of the carrier is transformed to a _____ IF.

*

— — — — — — — — — — — —

frequency-modulated

7-105. After amplification through the IF strip, the IF is applied to the *frequency discriminator* which performs a job comparable to that of a _____.
*

— — — — — — — — — — — — — — — —

detector

7-106. The frequency discriminator converts the _____ variations into _____ variations and filters out the IF components
*

— — — — — — — — — — — — — — — —

frequency
amplitude

7-107. The output of the frequency discriminator is an _____ signal which is a *duplicate* of the one used for _____ in the transmitter.
*

— — — — — — — — — — — — — — — —

audio
modulation

7-108. After the discriminator, the audio is processed through a *deemphasis* network which *does not* appear on our block diagram. The deemphasis network *alters the bias* on the audio amplifier so that *gain is inversely proportional to frequency*. This removes the distortion which was added in the transmitter by the _____ network.
*

— — — — — — — — — — — — — — — —

preemphasis

7-109. This is a block diagram of a *practical* single side band
receiver.

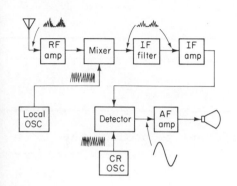

The single side band input is *mixed*
with the local oscillator frequency to
produce a single _____ _____ IF.

*

side band

7-110. The IF filter *prevents* RF components from passing with the IF.
It passes the single side band ____ which is amplified through the IF
strip and applied to the _____ .

*

IF

detector

7-111. CR is an abbreviation for *carrier reinsertion*. The CR oscillator produces a continuous RF signal which is *equivalent* to the missing RF carrier. This _____ carrier is mixed with the IF in the _____ to restore any missing component of intelligence.

*

—— —— —— —— —— —— —— —— —— —— —— ——

reinserted

detector

7-112. The *detector* then rectifies and filters to produce the _____ signal.

*

—— —— —— —— —— —— —— —— —— —— —— ——

audio

SUMMARY

1. A *transmitter* generates a carrier wave, impresses it with intelligence, and radiates it into space.

2. The *type of modulation* used identifies the type of transmitter.

3. AM, FM, and single side band are *common* transmitter types.

4. The *AM transmitter* impresses the intelligence on the amplitude of a carrier wave.

5. The *FM transmitter* impresses the intelligence into the frequency of the carrier wave.

6. The *single side band transmitter* suppresses the carrier and one side band. The intelligence is amplitude modulated into the remaining side band.

7. The *microphone* converts sound waves into electric audio signals which are used to modulate a carrier wave.

8. The *carrier wave* is generated by an RF oscillator, but this frequency may be *multiplied* a number of times before transmission

9. The *AM transmitter* modulates by using the audio signal to control the *gain* of an RF power amplifier.

10. The *FM transmitter* modulates by using the audio signal to control the *frequency* of the RF oscillator.

11. The *upper side band* in AM is the *sum* of the carrier frequency and the audio frequency. The *lower side band* is the *difference* between these two frequencies.

12. In the *FM transmitter*, the audio signal varies the frequency of the carrier.

13. The preemphasis network improves the signal to noise ratio of the FM signal by increasing the gain of the *high* frequency audio.

14. The *FM transmitter* has many side bands. Any side band that is *one percent* of the carrier amplitude is significant.

15. A *receiver* intercepts a carrier wave, amplifies it, and extracts the intelligence.

16. The receiver *types* match the transmitter types.

17. Most modern receivers use *heterodyning* to produce the IF. This is a process of *mixing* two frequencies and extracting the difference.

18. *Superheterodyne* is a term which indicates that the receiver uses heterodyning.

19. *Double conversion* is a statement indicating two stages of mixing.

20. *Detection* is a process of rectification and filtering.

21. In the *AM receiver*, a *detector* changes amplitude-modulated IF to audio signals.

22. In the *FM receiver*, a *frequency discriminator* does the job of a detector by changing frequency variations to amplitude variations.

23. In the *FM receiver* a *deemphasis* network removes the distortion caused by the *preemphasis* action in the transmitter.

24. The audio signals *drive* the speaker in the receiver and cause it to *reproduce* the sound waves which entered the microphone of the transmitter.

25. The *carrier reinsertion* oscillator is used in the single side band receiver to reinsert a frequency similar to the missing carrier wave.

SECTION 8
TRANSMISSION LINES AND ANTENNAS

Specifically we are interested in *RF transmission lines* that bridge the gap from the final transmitter stage to the antenna and from the receiving antenna to the first stage in the receiver. Any *pair* of wires may be used as such a transmission line, but such an arbitrary line would very likely waste more energy than it delivered. At these critical points in our communications chain we must be very conservative with our RF energy. Special transmission lines have been designed in an effort to minimize the loss of energy.

TYPES OF LINES
Open Wire Line

8-1. The open wire line is composed of a *pair* of noninsulated, parallel conductors as shown here.

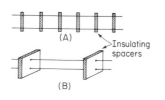

The conductors are separated by a fixed distance which is maintained by *insulated spacers* placed at suitable intervals. Two types of spacers are shown. Their only purpose is to maintain a _____ between the wires.

*

fixed distance

8-2. The spacing should never be *more than* 0.01 wave length of the frequency being carried. The line suffers some radiation loss anyway. Improper spacing causes radiation loss to *increase*. Proper spacing between conductors helps to keep down the _____ .
*

— — — — — — — — — — — —

radiation loss

8-3. Stringing the open wire line in the near vicinity of metallic objects will increase the radiation loss. The open line should not be placed near_____ objects.
*

— — — — — — — — — — — —

metallic

Stranded Wire Ribbon Line

8-4. The *stranded wire ribbon* line is an improvement over the open line. This line has insulation, and the insulation provides fixed spacing between the conductors. It is illustrated here.

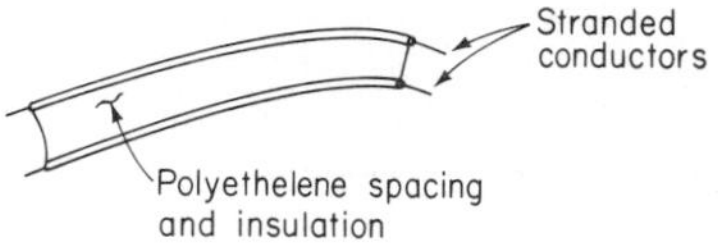

Stranded conductors

Polyethelene spacing and insulation

The _____ ribbon is familiar to most people because it is commonly used as the lead-in from receiving television antennas.

*

— — — — — — — — — — — —

stranded wire

8-5.   The wire strands are very thin which limits the use of this
line to *low power*, but it has less radiation loss than the open line.
The stranded wire ribbon has _____ radiation loss, but the open
pair can carry _____ power.
*

— — — — — — — — — — — — — — —

less
more

Shielded Line

8-6.   The *shielded line* has two conductors imbedded in insulation,
and a metal braid *shield* covers both conductors as shown here.

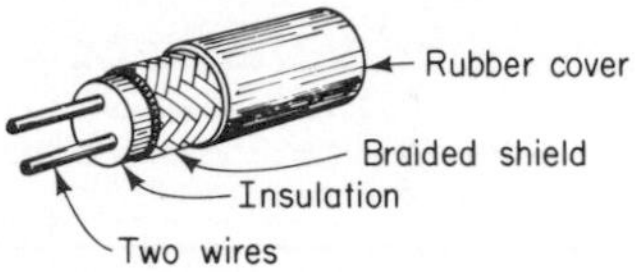

The flexible, internal insulation provides
insulation between the _____ and
between each conductor and the _____ .

conductors
metal shield

8-7.   The shield in turn is *surrounded* by another coat of tough
insulation. The metal braid shield is kept at *ground potential*.
This keeps the two conductors a _____ distance from ground and
completely isolates them from most outside _____ .
*

— — — — — — — — — — — — — — —

fixed
influences

8-8. The shielded line can carry relatively *high power* at frequencies up to *30 MHz*. It can be used underground, aboveground, and directly on metallic objects without a noticeable increase in losses. The metal shield enables this line to be used where other lines would suffer too much _____.

*

— — — — — — — — — — — — — — — —

loss

Coaxial Line

8-9. The *coaxial line* is closely related to the shielded line as this drawing indicates.

Copper braid
outer conductor
Polyethelyene
Wire inner conductor

One conductor is sealed in flexible insulation. The insulation is then wrapped with a *metal braid* which serves as the second _____.

*

— — — — — — — — — — — — — — — —

conductor

8-10. *Another coat* of insulation covers the metallic braid. The outer insulation is primarily a protective coating for the metal. A *1/2 inch* diameter coaxial line of this type can handle power of *one kilowatt* at frequencies up to *30 MHz*. This is an improvement in _____ capabilities over the previous lines.

*

— — — — — — — — — — — — — — — —

power

8-11. Coaxial lines feature *standard connectors* with quick connect features. The better connectors provide *moisture proofing*. The coaxial line is frequently called a *cable* and it is a very efficient and versatile line. It may be found inside steel bulkheads, under water, on poles, and underground. The coaxial line or cable is flexible enough for a _____ of applications and environmental _____ .

*

— — — — — — — — — — — — — —

variety
conditions

Wave Guides

8-12. As frequencies continued to *climb*, new types of transmission lines had to be found. The *wave guide* is one of these types. This drawing illustrates a section of two types of wave guides.

Round

Rectangular

The round and rectangular wave guides are the most popular design, but they can be built in *any desired shape*. They are called wave guides because they are *hollow* and microwave energy can be *piped* through them. Wave guides can be made in any desired_____ and microwave energy can be _____ through the hollow tube.

*

— — — — — — — — — — — — — —

shape
piped

8-13. The wave guide is a very *effective* transmission line for
_____ frequencies.

*

— — — — — — — — — — — — —

microwave

LINE CHARACTERISTICS

8-14. We have seen several types of lines. Now we will examine
some general *characteristics* of transmission lines. There are many
_____of lines but all possess certain _____
characteristics.

*

— — — — — — — — — — — — —

types
common (general)

8-15. The *physical* characteristics of a line determine how it will
react electrically, and each line has its *own limitations* of power
and frequency. Each line has its own limits of _____ and
_____, and the physical characteristics affect the _____
operation.

*

— — — — — — — — — — — — —

power
frequency
electric

8-16. All conductors have *resistance* and *inductance*, and when two conductors are placed close together, *capacitance* is present. All transmission lines have _____ , _____ , and _____ .

*

— — — — — — — — — — — — — —

resistance

inductance

capacitance

8-17. Since low resistance materials are used, the dc resistance is *negligible* unless the line is very long. This leaves the _____ and _____ which offer opposition to ac.

*

— — — — — — — — — — — — — —

inductance

capacitance

8-18. Inductance and capacitance are *distributed* along the full length of the line as shown in this drawing.

In the transmitter, the *signal source* is the final stage of RF power amplification, and the *destination* is the _____ . In the receiver, the source is the antenna, and the destination is the _____ of RF amplification.

*

— — — — — — — — — — — — — —

antenna

first stage

8-19. All *along* the transmission line, the *signal path* is composed of series_____ and parallel _____ .
*

─ ─ ─ ─ ─ ─ ─ ─ ─ ─ ─ ─

inductors
capacitors

8-20. *Physical* characteristics, such as size and shape of the conductors, type of material, distance separating them, and type of insulation, *determine* the amount of _____ and _____ per unit length of the line.
*

─ ─ ─ ─ ─ ─ ─ ─ ─ ─ ─ ─

inductance
capacitance

Characteristic Impedance

8-21. *Characteristic impedance* is the impedance of a particular transmission line which has no termination point. Physically, such a line is impossible, but it can be constructed electrically. A *nonresonant* line has E and I in phase at all points on the line which makes the impedance the same as a pure _____ .
*

─ ─ ─ ─ ─ ─ ─ ─ ─ ─ ─ ─

resistance

8-22. The characteristic impedance is Z_o and $Z_o = $ L/C. When a nonresonant line is terminated in this characteristic impedance, electrically it is an *infinitely long* line. When a nonresonant line is terminated in its characteristic impedance, it behaves as if it has no _____ .

*

— — — — — — — — — — — — — — — —

termination point

8-23. In the *infinitely long* line, E and I are in phase and the _____ is pure resistance. , In this line Z_o is also equal to E x I.

*

— — — — — — — — — — — — — — — —

characteristic impedance

8-24. A *section* of line has a capacitance of 30 pF and an inductance of 0.15 μH. The characteristic impedance is_____ohms.

*

— — — — — — — — — — — — — — — —

70.7

8-25. Electrically the line is composed of an infinite number of such sections, and each section exhibits the characteristic _____ .

*

— — — — — — — — — — — — — — — —

impedance

8-26. When the line is terminated properly, nearly all the energy is *delivered* to the load, and the load *absorbs* all the energy received. In order for the load to receive and use full energy, the line must be _____ with a resistor equal to_____.
*

— — — — — — — — — — — — — —

terminated

Z_o

Electromagnetic Energy

8-27. A potential difference between two lines sets up an *electric field* between the lines similar to that between the plates of a capacitor. This field is reversed for each *half-wave* distance along the line. This drawing illustrates the field and the RF potential which causes it.

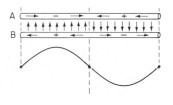

The arrows indicate the direction of the *field* which is the same direction that a _____ charge would move if placed in the field.

*

— — — — — — — — — — — — — —

positive

8-28. The wave shape is taken *from* conductor B with *respect* to A. The direction of the _____ and the _____ changes for each half-wave distance on the line.

*
— — — — — — — — — — — — — — —

field
current

8-29. In addition to the electric field, a *magnetic field* surrounds each conductor as illustrated here.

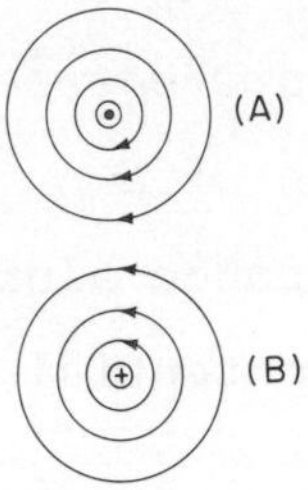

This is an *end view* of a two wire line. *Current* is entering B and emerging from A. The *flux lines* encircle B in a _____ direction and are _____ around A.

*
— — — — — — — — — — — — — — —

counterclockwise
clockwise

8-30. In the area represented *between* the conductors, all *magnetic* (H) lines are in the same direction. All *electric* (E) lines are also in a constant direction. The A section of this drawing shows the pattern of E and H lines at the same instant as depicted in frame 8-29. The B section shows it on the next alternation of the RF potential.

The E lines are from _____ to _____ and the H lines are _____ to them. Both E and H lines reverse directions when the RF signal changes _____ .

*

— — — — — — — — — — — — — — — —

positive

negative

perpendicular

polarity (direction)

8-31. These combined *E and H fields* advance down the line from source to load. The *rate* of travel is determined by the conducting medium and the signal frequency. The fields start at the entrance to the line with the first increment of applied voltage. These lines are pushed away from the sources as new fields build up to match every change of input signal. The combined E and H fields start at the _____ and travel toward the _____ .

*

— — — — — — — — — — — — — — — —

source

load

8-32. The field *propagation* rate is determined by the propagation
_____ and the signal _____ .

*

— — — — — — — — — — — — — — —

medium
frequency

_____

8-33. The signal *changes polarities*, the current *changes direction*,
the E and H lines *reverse direction*, but the direction of propagation
is constant from _____ to _____ .

*

— — — — — — — — — — — — — — —

source
load

Wave Length
_____

8-34. Wave length (λ) is velocity (V) divided by frequency (f).
λ is in meters, V is velocity of light in meters (300,000,000), and
f is signal frequency in hertz. The formula is greatly simplified
by using f in MHz and removing 6 zeros from the velocity; thus,
λ = 300/f. The wave length of a 60 Hz signal is about_____statute
miles; for 300 MHz it is about _____ meter (1 meter is 39.4 inches).

*

— — — — — — — — — — — — — — —

3100
one

8-35. The speed of light is the *reference* velocity for all electro-magnetic propagation. This is 300,000,000 meters per second, 186,000 miles per second, or 984 feet per microsecond. The speed of light in free space is _____ meters per second.
*

— — — — — — — — — — — — — — —

300,000,000

8-36. All *electromagnetic propagation* in space is the same as the speed of light, and a given frequency covers a distance of *one wave length for each period* of the signal. The speed of light and the speed of all other electromagnetic propagation in free space is _____ meters per second or a distance of one wave length per _____ of the signal.
*

— — — — — — — — — — — — — — —

300,000,000
period

8-37. In a transmission line, propagation is still one wave length per period, but the wave length is *shortened*. The amount of shortening is determined by the conducting medium. Propagation in any medium is one wave length per _____ , but the wave length is different with each _____ medium.
*

— — — — — — — — — — — — — — —

signal period
different

8-38. The velocity of *propagation (VP) constant* is a percentage figure which compares the velocity in a medium with the velocity in free space. If the medium has a VP of 95%, the wave length is *shortened* by 5% and the *velocity* of propagation is reduced by 5%. How many feet per microsecond will a wave travel in a transmission line with a VP of 97%?

*

— — — — — — — — — — — —

954.48

8-39. The length of a transmission line is measured in *wave lengths* of the designated frequency within that line. The VP constant is already taken into consideration. How many feet are in a 10 wave length line at 30 MHz if the VP is 95%?

*

— — — — — — — — — — — —

311.9 (or exactly 311 feet and 11 inches)

Energy Distribution

8-40. In a properly *terminated* line, the energy travels as a *wave front*. All points of the line experience all the values of current and voltage as each period of the signal propagates past. At any given instant, all values of current and voltage could be found in any *wave length section* of the line. The wave front is in constant motion, and any point in the line experiences all values once each

_____ .

*

— — — — — — — — — — — —

wave length (period)

8-41. This drawing illustrates the conditions in a line at one particular *instant* of time.

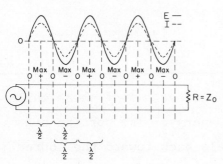

From any point, a *full-wave length* distance in either direction, the exact conditions are *repeated*; a *half-wave length* in either direction finds the same amplitude but opposite phase.

Any *even number of half-waves* in either direction finds _____ conditions.

Any *odd number of half-waves* in either direction finds _____ polarities.

*
--- --- --- --- --- --- --- --- --- --- ---

identical

reversed

RESONANT LINES

8-42. When a transmission line is terminated in any manner except a resistance equal to Z_o, it becomes a *resonant line*. This is a *mismatch* of impedance, energy is *reflected* from the load, and the line suffers a *loss* of power. A line terminated in any manner except Z_o is a _____ line.

*
--- --- --- --- --- --- --- --- --- --- ---

resonant

8-43. A resonant line has a *mismatch* of impedance which results in
_____ energy and power _____ .

*

— —

reflected

loss

8-44. The resonant line has voltage and current *out of phase* which
enables the load to use only part of the energy. The portion not
used is *reflected* from the load and travels back toward the source.
Direct and reflected waves combine and become *standing waves* along
the line. The reflected energy is a loss. Because voltage and
current are out of phase, the load _____ part of the energy and
_____ the rest back toward the source. The _____
energy is lost energy.

*

— —

uses

reflects

reflected

8-45. A resonant line is assumed to have the *resonant* frequency
applied to it because the line can be resonant to only one frequency.
The term resonance implies a particular _____ .

*

— —

frequency

8-46.   A line terminated in an *open* is a resonant line.   The open
end is an *infinite* impedance which is equivalent to a *parallel*
resonant circuit.   At the open end, voltage is maximum and current
is minimum.   Maximum impedance, maximum voltage, and minimum current
are the conditions of _____ , and all of these
appear at the _____ end of a resonant line.
*

— — — — — — — — — — — — — —

parallel resonance
open

8-47.   Any *odd* number of *quarter-wave* lengths back from the open end
of a resonant line, there is a condition of series resonance: minimum impedance (almost zero), minimum voltage, and maximum current.
At the open end the line is _____ ; one quarter-
wave length from the open is a reflected _____, a condition of
_____ .
*

— — — — — — — — — — — — — —

parallel resonant
short
series resonance

8-48.   The same *series* resonant conditions exist at three, five, and
any other_____ quarter-wave length from the open.
*

— — — — — — — — — — — — — —

odd

351

8-49. Any *even* number of *quarter wave* lengths from the open, there is a reflected *open* which is a repetition of the _____ _____ condition.

*

― ― ― ― ― ― ― ― ― ― ― ―

parallel resonant

8-50. This drawing illustrates the relation of Z, E, and I at various quarter wave lengths from an *open*.

8-50

Even quarter-wave lengths from the open are a reflected _____. *Odd* quarter wave lengths from the open are a reflected _____.

*

― ― ― ― ― ― ― ― ― ― ― ―

open

short

8-51. For distances *other than* exact multiples of quarter-wave lengths, the open end line is either inductive or capacitive. For instance, *less than a quarter*, the line is capacitor; *more than a quarter* but less than a half, the line is an inductor. An open end line less than a quarter-wave long is a _____; more than one-quarter and less than two it is an _____.

*

― ― ― ― ― ― ― ― ― ― ― ―

capacitor

inductor

Shorted End Line

8-52. When a resonant line is terminated in a *short*, the shorted end is *zero* impedance and has maximum current and zero voltage. This is _____.
*

— — — — — — — — — — — — — —

series resonance

8-53. All *even* quarter-wave lengths from the *short* have reflected shorts which also constitute _____.
*

— — — — — — — — — — — — — —

series resonance

8-54. All *odd* quarter-wave lengths from the *short* have reflected opens which constitute _____.
*

— — — — — — — — — — — — — —

parallel resonance

8-55.   This drawing illustrates the relation of E, I, and Z at various quarter-wave lengths from a *short*.

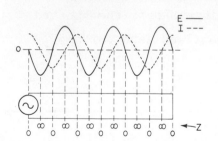

Three quarter-wave lengths from the short, we have _____ resonance; *four* quarter-wave lengths from the short, we have _____ resonance.

*
— — — — — — — — — — —

parallel
series

8-56. This drawing illustrates the conditions in open and shorted lines for *all parts* of a complete wave length.

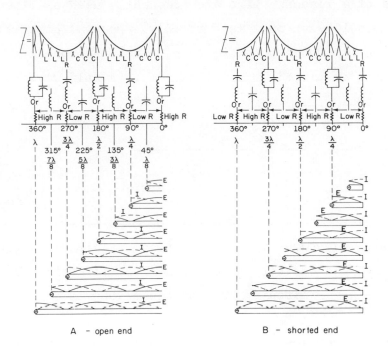

A – open end   B – shorted end

A quarter-wave short is an _____; a quarter-wave open is a
_____.

*
— — — — — — — — — — — — —

open

short

Uses of Resonant Sections

8-57. Sections of a resonant line are frequently used as circuit *components*. The half-wave open is a *parallel resonant* circuit; it can be used as an *impedance matching* transformer. Resonant sections of a line are used as circuit ______________. A half-wave open section makes a good ______________.

*

--- --- --- --- --- --- --- --- --- --- --- ---

components

transformer

8-58. The *quarter-wave open* is a *series resonant* circuit; it can be used as a *filter*. The quarter-wave open will perform the jobs of a __________________ circuit. One of these jobs is ____________.

*

--- --- --- --- --- --- --- --- --- --- --- ---

series resonant

filtering

8-59. The quarter-wave short is a ____________ resonant circuit. It is often used as a metallic *insulator*.

*

--- --- --- --- --- --- --- --- --- --- --- ---

parallel

8-60. An undesirable frequency can be *eliminated* from your receiver with a section of transmission line as shown here.

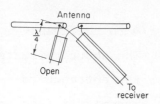

The quarter-wave open section is a quarter-wave length to the *undesired* frequency. To this frequency, the line to the receiver has a _____ across the entrance.

*
— — — — — — — — — — — —

short

8-61. If the problem is *selecting* a particular band of frequencies, it can be solved in this manner.

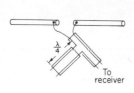

The quarter-wave section is cut to a quarter-wave length to the center frequency of the *desired* band. It is then connected in series with one conductor of the _____.

*
— — — — — — — — — — — —

transmission line

8-62. The open reflects a _____ across the section entrance for the selected _____ and a narrow band. All other frequencies find an _____ transmission line.

*
— — — — — — — — — — — —

short

frequency

open

8-63. This drawing illustrates the *use* of shorted quarter-wave
length sections for support, insulation, and harmonic filters all
in one.

The sections are $\lambda/4$ to the transmitter frequency. The short reflects
an _____ across the entrance to
the line. To the transmitter frequency
these sections are good _____ .

*
— — — — — — — — — — — — — —

open

insulators

8-64. The shorted end of these sections is frequently *welded* to
steel plates to give support to the transmission line. Such an
action causes no loss for the _____ frequency.

*
— — — — — — — — — — — — — —

resonant

8-65. The same sections that are $\lambda/4$ to the resonant frequency are
$\lambda/2$ to the second harmonic and even $\lambda/4$ to all even harmonics.
These insulating supports are then very effective _____ filters.

*
— — — — — — — — — — — — — —

harmonic

8-66. This drawing illustrates the use of a λ/4 shorted section in *matching* impedances.

One end of the λ/4 section is zero; the other is _____.

*

_ _ _ _ _ _ _ _ _ _ _ _

infinity

8-67. Some place between the two ends lies points of any *desired* impedance. The impedance is matched by connecting the 300 ohm line to the _____ ohm point on the λ/4 section and the 70 ohm line to the _____ ohm point on the same λ/4 section.
*

_ _ _ _ _ _ _ _ _ _ _ _

300
70

LOSSES IN TRANSMISSION LINES

8-68. There are basically *three* types of losses in a transmission line: *copper* loss, *dielectric* loss, and *radiation* loss. A transmission has copper loss, _____ loss, and _____ loss.
*

_ _ _ _ _ _ _ _ _ _ _ _

dielectric
radiation

8-69. Copper loss is an I^2R loss due to conductor resistance. This becomes more pronounced at high frequencies. Electron movement is retarded inside the conductor and travels mostly in a *thin surface layer*. This is known as *skin effect*. The skin effect electrically reduces the cross sectional area and causes a greater power loss. Copper loss _____ at high frequencies because the cross sectional area of the conductor is effectively _____.

*

— — — — — — — — — — — — —

increases

reduced

8-70. . The tendency of electrons to travel on the *surface* of the conductor is _____ , and it increases the _____ loss at high frequencies.

*

— — — — — — — — — — — — —

skin effect

copper

8-71. *Dielectric loss* is caused from *heating* the insulating material around and between the conductors. The changing fields distort the electron paths of the dielectric material. This constant agitation produces heat and the heat represents a dissipation of energy. Energy lost due to insulation heating is a _____ loss.

*

— — — — — — — — — — — — —

dielectric

8-72. *Radiation loss* is caused from the fact that some lines of force are unable to return to the conductor when the field reverses. A certain amount of energy is *radiated* out with these lines of force. Open lines are most susceptible to radiation loss. When lines of force are radiated from a line, they carry off a certain quantity of _____ . This is _____ loss.

*

—— —— —— —— —— —— —— —— —— —— —— —— ——

energy

radiation

8-73. *Induction loss* is so closely related to radiation loss that the two are generally lumped together. Induction loss occurs when an unshielded line is placed near a metallic object. The flux from the line *induces* a current into the adjacent metal. This is a *transformer* action, and it saps energy from the line. Any time flux from a conductor cuts a conducting object, current is_____ in that object with a resulting _____ loss of energy from the transmission line.

*

—— —— —— —— —— —— —— —— —— —— —— —— ——

induced

induction

8-74. All the losses discussed here became more pronounced with each frequency *increase*. The wave guide was constructed as a transmission line for microwave frequencies in an effort to *reduce the losses*. Wave guides are _____ for _____ frequencies. The losses on other lines increased as frequencies _____ until they became impractical.

*

— — — — — — — — — — — — — —

transmission lines

microwave

increased

WAVE GUIDES

8-75. It is a small step from the coaxial line to a wave guide. A round wave guide is essentially a coaxial line with the *center* conductor and insulation *removed*. This leaves a metal *tube* or pipe, and electromagnetic energy can be propagated through this pipe. A round wave guide is a hollow, metallic _____ which is used to carry _____ energy.

*

— — — — — — — — — — — — — —

tube (pipe)

electromagnetic

8-76. Wave guide sections are constructed in almost any desirable *shape* and the coupling resembles *plumbing* more than it does electric connections. Here are some sample wave guide sections.

This shows four sections of a _____ wave guide, and each section is constructed in a different _____.

*

rectangular

shape

8-77. The theory of *construction* is very simple. An infinite number of λ/4 shorted sections is connected to the two wires of a transmission line. This principle is illustrated here.

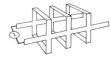

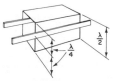

After a large number of sections are added and joined together, a box, or a tube, is formed with the two conductors in the _____ of opposite _____.

*

center

walls

8-78.   Current and voltage are present in the *wide walls* where the
conductors theoretically exist, but propagation inside the cavity
is our primary concern.   This propagation resembles *wave propagation*
in space.   Propagation in a _____ resembles propagation
in _____ and is considered apart from voltage and _____ .
*

- - - - - - - - - - - - - -

wave guide

space

current

8-79.   One method of *inserting* energy into a wave guide is illustrated
here.

Radiating probe

In this case, the probe _____ energy
directly into the cavity.

*

- - - - - - - - - - - - - -

radiates

8-80. The widening circle from the probe *encounters* both walls of the guide at an angle and the walls reflect the energy at a corresponding angle. As the energy waves encounter the _____ , they are reflected back at an _____ .

*

— — — — — — — — — — — —

walls

angle

8-81. The *wave front* progresses down the guide diagonally. Each time a wall is encountered, the wave is *reflected* and the phase is *reversed*. This is illustrated by this drawing.

The wave front travels _____ from the source in a _____ pattern.

Wave front traveling in direction A

Wall of waveguide

Wavefront traveling in direction B

8-81

*

— — — — — — — — — — — —

away

zig-zag

8-82. In order for a wave to exist, both *electric and magnetic* fields must be present. The E and H lines form complex patterns inside the wave guide, and the conditions repeat at distances of $\lambda/2$. The entire field is *contained* within the cavity. Complex patterns of _____ lines exist within the wave guide. These patterns repeat at distances of _____ wave lengths.

*

——

E and H

half-

——

8-83. This end view illustrates the E and H pattern at one *instant*. The E lines are _____ to the *wide walls* and *tangent* to the narrow walls. The H lines are _____ _____ to the wide walls and to the H lines.

E - line tangent to surface of wall

H - lines are perpendicular to top

H - lines are interrupted

H - field - - →
E - field ———→

*

——

parallel

perpendicular

8-84. All lines are in *constant motion*, and when polarity changes, each line changes direction by 180°. The E and H lines both _____ directions with each change of _____ .

*

reverse
polarity

8-85. Energy can be coupled *from wave guides* in many ways: probes, resonant cavities, windows, and feed horns. A flared feed horn on the end of a wave guide can radiate energy *without* the necessity for an antenna. Energy can be removed from a wave guide by_____, resonant cavities, and _____ . It can also be radiated directly from a flared_____ .

*

probes
windows
feed horn

8-86. The transmitting *antenna* is an active device which couples electromagnetic energy to free space. It is driven by relatively high power levels to cause a strong energy radiation. The transmitting antenna is an _____ device for coupling electromagnetic energy to free_____. It is driven by high_____to cause strong_____.
*

— — — — — — — — — — — — — —

active
space
power
radiation

8-87. The receiving antenna is a *passive piece of conducting material* which has current induced into it by the electromagnetic waves which contact the metal. Any piece of_____conducting material may be a _____ antenna. Electromagnetic waves striking the receiving antenna_____a current.
*

— — — — — — — — — — — — — —

passive
receiving
induce

8-88. Any transmitting antenna may *also* be used for reception, and receiver antennas are greatly *refined* for the most efficient reception of weak signals. While any conductor may serve as a _____ antenna, many refinements are made for the most efficient _____ of weak signals.

*

— — — — — — — — — — — — — —

receiving
reception

Electromagnetic Radiation

8-89. An effective antenna can be constructed by *folding* a λ/4 section of transmission line as shown here.

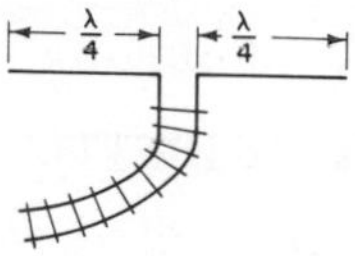

This is a *half-wave dipole* with each half formed from a quarter-wave section of a _____.

*

— — — — — — — — — — — — — —

conductor

8-90. The fold being made a *quarter-wave* from the open end places it at a point of reflected _____ impedance.

*

— — — — — — — — — — — — — —

zero

369

8-91. At the fold, voltage is *zero* and current is *maximum* at each end of the antenna; a quarter-wave from the fold, the voltage is _____ and the current is _____ .

*

— — — — — — — — — — — — — — —

maximum
minimum

8-92. At any given point in a transmission line currents in the two conductors are in *opposite* directions. This is also true for the two quarter-wave sections of our antenna. The current is going out on one section as it returns on the other. Looking at the antenna as one line, the two currents are *additive*. This drawing shows current and voltage relations.

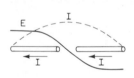

Voltage is *constantly changing amplitude* and periodically reversing _____ . Current is *constantly changing amplitude* and periodically reversing _____ .

*

— — — — — — — — — — — — — — —

polarity
direction

8-93. Both voltage and current are *changing* at a very rapid sinusoidal rate. The E and H lines *build up and decay* in synchronization with the current. The changing voltage causes changing _____ which causes a constant build up and decay of _____ lines.

*

— — — — — — — — — — — —

current

E and H

8-94. The H lines *encircle* the antenna at all points. This drawing is a partial representation.

H lines

With each reversal of current, the H lines _____ into the line, reverse _____ , and build up again.

*

— — — — — — — — — — — —

decay

directions

8-95. The E lines *surround* the antenna in a pattern similar to this.

E lines

The E and H lines build up, decay, and reverse directions at the same time. The E lines are _____ to the H lines at all times.

*

— — — — — — — — — — — —

perpendicular

8-96. As the fields build up, decay, and reverse directions, some of the lines become *trapped in space*. This is illustrated in these drawings.

These drawings represent the _____lines only, but they are accompanied by_____ lines.

— — — — — — — — — — — —

E

H

8-97. In drawing A, current is *maximum*, and the _____field is fully expanded.

*

— — — — — — — — — — — —

E

8-98. In drawing B, current has decreased to a *minimum*, and the E lines are _____ into the antenna.

*

— — — — — — — — — — — —

decaying

8-99. In drawing C, the current has *reversed* direction, and some of the E lines are _____ before they can completely collapse.

*

— — — — — — — — — — — —

trapped

8-100. In drawing D, current is *building up*, and the reversed E field is _____ .

*

- - - - - - - - - - - - -

expanding

8-101. The *trapped E lines* form complete loops and are in the same direction as the new field expanding from the antenna. Lines in the same direction *repel* each other. Therefore, the expanding field _____ the trapped field into space at the speed of _____ .

*

- - - - - - - - - - - - -

drives (repels)
light

8-102. The *E and H field* repelled from the antenna travels through space at 186,000 miles per second expanding as it goes. The lines retain the same direction they had when they left the antenna. The E lines are _____ to the antenna and the H lines are _____ to the E lines.

*

- - - - - - - - - - - - -

parallel
perpendicular

8-103. At points along the propagation path separated by a *half-wave length* both E and H lines are in opposite directions. This pattern in space is similar to that in the _____ .

*

- - - - - - - - - - - - -

wave guide

8-104. The position of the antenna in respect to the earth's surface is the antenna *polarization*. A vertical antenna is *vertically*
polarized, and it radiates E lines in a vertical position. A horizontal antenna is *horizontally* polarized, and it radiates E lines
in a horizontal position. The polarization of an antenna is its
position relative to the _____ _____ , and the radiated
E lines are _____ to the antenna.
*
— — — — — — — — — — — — — — — — —

earth's surface
parallel

RECEIVING ELECTROMAGNETIC ENERGY

8-105. For *maximum* reception of electromagnetic energy, the receiving
antenna should be polarized in the same plane as the transmitting
antenna. If the transmitting antenna is vertical, the receiving
antenna should be _____ .
*
— — — — — — — — — — — — — — — —

vertical

8-106. The wave front approaches the receiving antenna as a *huge
sheet* of very weak energy. This sheet is composed of a grid-work
of E and H lines. The front passes at 186,000 miles per second
followed by a continuous electromagnetic field. The wave front is
a sheet of _____ composed of a grid-work of __ ___ __lines.
*
— — — — — — — — — — — — — — — —

energy
E and H

374

8-107. If the receiving antenna is properly polarized, the approach-
ing *H lines* will be *perpendicular* to the antenna. As the field
passes, the H lines cut across the antenna and *induce* a current.
Proper polarization places the receiving antenna _____
to the oncoming H lines. The H lines _____ the antenna and
_____ current.
*

perpendicular
cut
induce

8-108. The transmitting antenna is the *primary* of a transformer,
and the receiving antenna is the *secondary*. The primary and secondary may be separated by many miles of space, but they couple usable
energy across this space. A pair of antennas composes a _____
with the transmitting antenna being the _____ and the receiving
antenna the _____ .
*

transformer
primary
secondary

8-109. The transmitting antenna changes electric energy to *electromagnetic* energy and couples it into space. The receiving antenna intercepts the electromagnetic energy and changes it back to *electric energy*. The transmitting antenna converts _____ energy to _____ energy. The receiving antenna converts _____ to _____ energy.

*

— — — — — — — — — — — —

electric
electromagnetic
electromagnetic
electric

TYPES OF ANTENNAS
Marconi

8-110. The *Marconi* is a half-wave antenna. Half of it is a physical section of antenna a λ/4 long. The other half is an *image reflection* of this quarter-wave section. The Marconi antenna consists of a _____ section and an _____ .

*

— — — — — — — — — — — —

quarter-wave
image reflection

8-111. The quarter-wave section is mounted *vertically* on a conducting surface. The surface reflects the $\lambda/4$ section. The physical section is *shorted* to the conducting surface. The better the conductor, the better the results. Some surfaces that produce results are earth, water, and metal. A $\lambda/4$ section mounted vertically to a conducting surface forms a _____ half-wave antenna. Half of this antenna is a _____ from the conducting surface.

*

— — — — — — — — — — — — —

Marconi

reflection

8-112. This drawing illustrates the *Marconi* antenna.

The current and voltage react exactly as if the _____ were a real antenna.

*

— — — — — — — — — — — — —

image

Folded Dipole

8-113. This is the *folded dipole*.

It is formed by connecting a section of conductor parallel to an ordinary dipole. The conductor is connected to both ends of the _____.

*

— — — — — — — — — — — — —

dipole

8-114. The plain dipole may have an impedance as low as *15 ohms*. This is difficult to match to the *high* impedance of the transmission line. Adding the folded section *multiplies* the impedance by four. It is easier to match the impedance of a folded dipole than it is a plain dipole because the folded dipole has about _____ as much impedance.

*

— — — — — — — — — — — — —

four times

8-115. One section of the dipole is *fed* directly from the transmission line and the other is *excited by radiation* from the first. Currents in both elements are in the *same direction* which increases the field intensity. Current in the folded section is generated by _____ from the active section. This current is in phase with the current in the _____ section.

*

— — — — — — — — — — — — —

radiation
active

Directional Antennas

8-116. Since electromagnetic waves can be *directed* in a fashion similar to directing a *beam of light*, antennas can be made to radiate or receive in a directional pattern. Electromagnetic waves can be _____ , and antennas can be made to radiate or receive in a _____ pattern.

*

— — — — — — — — — — — —

directed
directional

8-117. An antenna is made *directional* by adding reflectors and directors to shape the beam pattern. Antennas are made directional by adding _____ and _____ .
*

_____ ___ ___ ____ _____ ____ ___ ___ ___ ___ ___ ____ ____

reflectors
directors

8-118. Most television receiver antennas are of a directional type known as a *parasitic array*. It is also called a *yagi*. A yagi or parasitic array is one type of _____ receiving antenna.
*

_____ ___ ___ ____ _____ ____ ___ ___ ___ ___ ___ ____ ____

directional

8-119. A yagi is usually composed of from *four to seven* elements. One element is *active*, and the others are *parasitic* reflectors and directors. Of the four to seven _____ of a yagi, one is _____ and the others are _____ reflectors and directors.
*

_____ ___ ___ ____ _____ ____ ___ ___ ___ ___ ___ ____ ____

elements
active
parasitic

8-120. A parasitic element 5% longer than the antenna and placed about a λ/4 away is a *reflector*. The reflector is slightly longer than the _____ and is about a _____ away from it.
*

_____ ___ ___ ____ _____ ____ ___ ___ ___ ___ ___ ____ ____

antenna
λ/4

379

8-121. A parasitic element that is 5% shorter than the antenna and placed about a λ/4 away is a *director*. The director is _____ than the antenna.

*

— — — — — — — — — — — — — — — —

shorter

8-122. This is a *four* element yagi.

Directors — Streamlined insulating bullard — Antenna — Reflector — Two-wire shielded cable

4 elements yagi using folded dipole

It consists of a _____ antenna, two _____ and a _____.

*

— — — — — — — — — — — — — — — —

folded dipole
directors
reflector

8-123. The *shortest* element on a yagi is the *front*, and all elements forward of the antenna are *directors*. The *longest* element is the *reflector*, and it is mounted on the *back* of the array. The electromagnetic energy is *beamed* forward and may have a directivity pattern as narrow as 50°. The yagi is not highly directional, but it may have a beam as narrow as _____ degrees.

*

— — — — — — — — — — — — — — — —

50

FACTORS AFFECTING WAVE PROPAGATION

8-124.   Some of the *factors* which either aid or hinder wave propagation are: type of antenna, surrounding terrain, height of antenna,
direction of radiation, weather conditions, the time of year, the
time of day, obstructions, and sun spots. This list contains only
a few factors which affect _____. Some of these
and others _____ .
*

___ __ _ __ _ __ __ ___ _ __ __ _ __ __ ___

propagation
aid
hinder

Types of Waves

8-125.   As energy fans out from the transmitting antenna, it resembles
a huge, invisible *doughnut* with the antenna threaded through the hole.
The curved surface of the doughnut represents the expanding *wave
front*. Energy fans out from the _____ antenna like a large
_____ .
*

___ __ _ __ _ __ __ __ __ _ __ __ _ __ __ ___

transmitting
doughnut

8-126. Some segments of this doughnut surface are moving at an elevated angle and are called *sky waves*. Some segments move horizontally
and are called *direct waves*. Other segments move at a downward
angle and are called *ground waves*. These waves are illustrated in
this drawing.

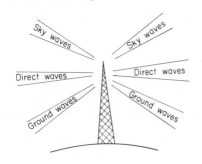

Sky waves travel at an _____ angle.
Direct waves travel_____ to the
earth's surface. Ground waves move on a
_____ angle.

*
— — — — — — — — — — —

elevated
parallel
downward

8-127. *Ground waves* travel along the surface of the earth for a
distance determined by terrain, weather conditions, and frequency.
30 MHz can usually reach 75 miles. 250 MHz, under ideal conditions,
may reach 1000 miles. Frequency,_____ , and_____ affect
the distance covered by_____ waves.
*
— — — — — — — — — — —

terrain
weather
ground

8-128. The *sky waves* are responsible for most long range communications. They *bounce* back and forth from ground to ionosphere and establish reliable, long distance links. Sky waves bounce back and forth from earth to _____ and are _____ means of long range radio communications.

*

— — — — — — — — — — — — — —

ionosphere
reliable

The Ionosphere

8-130. The *upper atmosphere* is composed of four *rarefied* layers of ionized gases known as the *ionosphere*. From the earth outward, these layers are D, E, F_1, and F_2 as shown in this drawing.

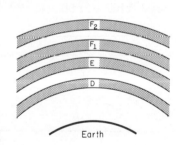

The E layer weakens at night, and the two F layers combine and move closer to the earth. During daylight hours the layers are _____ _____. At night they become _____.

*

— — — — — — — — — — — — — —

D, E, F_1, and F_2
D, E, and F

8-131.   The ionosphere acts as a conductor and *absorbs* energy from electromagnetic waves.   It also *refracts* waves of frequencies below 30 MHz, especially when they enter the ionosphere at an angle less than 90°.   The ionosphere _____ energy and _____ waves with frequencies below _____ MHz.

*

— — — — — — — — — — — — — — — — —

absorbs

refracts

30

8-132.   It should be emphasized that refraction is a *gradual bending* effect rather than a reflection.   The ionosphere *does not* _____ the waves.   It _____ them back toward the earth.

*

— — — — — — — — — — — — — — — — —

reflect

bends (refracts)

8-133. This drawing illustrates the effect of two waves entering the ionosphere at different angles.

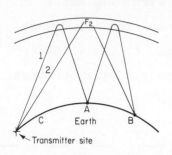

Wave 1 enters the ionosphere at a *steep angle* and is refracted at a steep angle. It strikes the earth, rebounds to the _____ , and is _____ back to earth a second time.

*

- - - - - - - - - - - - -

ionosphere

refracted

8-134. Wave 2 enters the ionosphere at a *low angle* and refracts at a low angle. It covers the same distance in one hop that wave 1 covers in _____ hops.

*

- - - - - - - - - - - - -

two

8-135. For wave 2, the zone from the transmitter to point B is *dead*. The wave *cannot* be received here, and it is called a *skip zone*. Wave 1 can be received at points A and B with skip zones between. *Ground waves* probably cover the distance from the transmitter to point C. There is *no reception* from ____to ____. Reception is possible at both A and B, but there is no reception between ____ and ____.

*

— — — — — — — — — — — — — —

C

A

A

B

SUMMARY

1. A *pair* of conductors which couples energy from one point to another is a *transmission line*.

2. The open line, the stranded ribbon, the coaxial, the shielded pair, and the wave guide are *examples* of transmission lines.

3. The stranded ribbon line is a good *low power line*.

4. The *coaxial line* can handle reasonable power at frequencies up to 30 MHz.

5. A hollow tube which carries electromagnetic energy is called a *wave guide*.

6. Any *two wire line* contains elements of resistance, inductance, and capacitance.

7. When *transmitting*, the signal *source* for the transmission line is the RF power amplifier and the *load* is the antenna.

8. When *receiving*, the signal *source* for the transmission line is the antenna and the *load* is the first RF amplifier.

9. An *infinitely long* line, or a line terminated in the characteristic impedance, absorbs all the energy. The voltage and current are in phase, and the impedance is pure resistance.

10. A line terminated in any manner except Z_o is a *resonant* line for some specific frequency.

11. The resonant line *reflects* part of its energy and creates standing waves along the line.

12. Both electric and magnetic *fields* exist in the area between the conductors of a transmission line.

13. The E and H lines are *perpendicular* to one another and both reverse direction each half-wave length.

14. In space, electromagnetic energy travels at the *speed of light* which is 300,000,000 meters per second, 186,000 miles per second, or 984 feet per microsecond.

15. Energy propagates a distance of *one wave length* during each period, but the wave length is shortened in a transmission line.

16. VP, the *velocity propagation factor,* is a percentage comparing the propagation speed in a medium with the speed of light.

17. Even $\lambda/4$ lengths from an *open*, the line is open; odd $\lambda/4$ lengths from an *open* is a reflected short.

18. Even $\lambda/4$ lengths from a *short,* the line is shorted; odd $\lambda/4$ lengths from a *short* is a reflected open.

19. The $\lambda/4$ shorted section can be *used* as a metallic insulator, line support, transformer, or harmonic filter.

20. A transmission line *suffers* from copper loss, dielectric loss, and radiation loss.

21. A *wave guide* is a transmission line for microwave frequencies.

22. Energy is *propagated* through a wave guide similar to free space propagation.

23. The transmitting antenna *couples* energy to free space.

24. The coupling from transmitter to receiver is similar to the action of a *transformer*.

25. *Radiation* is produced by the rapid reversal of current in the antenna. E and H fields become *trapped in space* and are repelled by the reversing field on the antenna.

26. *Electromagnetic energy* is propagated through space as a wave front moving and expanding at the speed of light.

27. *Both E and H fields* compose the electromagnetic waves. The E lines are parallel to the transmitting antenna and the H lines are perpendicular to the E lines.

28. The receiving antenna should be *polarized* the same as the transmitting antenna for maximum reception.

29. Current is *induced* into the receiving antenna by the H lines cutting across it.

30. *Sky waves* are radiated at an elevated angle. *Direct waves* are radiated parallel to the earth's surface. *Ground waves* are radiated at a downward angle.

31. The *ionosphere* consists of four layers of ionized gases. These are D, E, F_1, and F_2.

32. Sky waves are *refracted* from the ionosphere and rebound from the earth. They are responsible for most *reliable* long distance radio communications.

33. *Wave fronts* arrive at the receiving antenna as a sheet of energy composed of a grid-work of *E and H lines*.

SECTION 9
DEVICES WITH SPECIAL APPLICATIONS

The devices covered in this section have some *unique* design or *special* application. They *are not* necessarily either new or rare.

SOLID STATE RESISTORS

9-1.   Solid state materials have a *bothersome* characteristic of changing resistance with a change in temperature.   This characteristic has been turned to advantage in solid state *resistors*.   Solid state resistors capitalize on the fact that semiconductors are sensitive to _____ changes.

*

— — — — — — — — — — — —

temperature

Thermistor

9-2.   The *thermistor* is a solid state resistor with a resistance dependent upon the temperature.   Its construction is illustrated here. It is composed of two wire leads imbedded in a bead of _____ material.

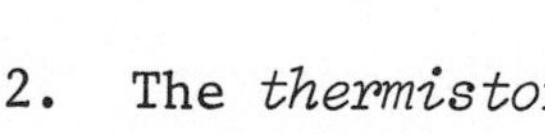

Wire   Semiconductor bead   Wire

*

— — — — — — — — — — — —

semiconductor

9-3. The thermistor has a *negative* temperature coefficient and can detect thermal changes as low as 0.0005° C. The extreme *sensitivity* of the _____ makes it valuable in detecting very _____ thermal changes.

*

— — — — — — — — — — — — — —

thermistor

small

9-4. Thermistors are *versatile* and are used for many things. Placed in series with a device with a positive temperature coefficient, the thermistor can *compensate* for the temperature change in the other component. Circuits can be built that are completely *immune* to wide changes in temperature. Circuits can be constructed with _____ in combination with other components that are _____ to a wide range of temperature change.

*

— — — — — — — — — — — — — —

thermistors

immune

9-5. This is an *indirectly* heated thermistor.

Protective seal
Heater
Thermister casing and heater form

The heater can maintain a *constant* temperature independently of the _____ through the thermistor.

*

— — — — — — — — — — — — — —

current

9-6. The indirectly heated thermistor can maintain a *constant* resistance despite temperature changes. It is also used in power meters for radio frequencies. In the latter application, RF is applied to the *heater* coil, and the *heating effect* is measured. Among other applications, the _____ heated thermistor can be the active element in the RF _____ _____.

*

— — — — — — — — — — — — — —

indirectly
power meter

Photoresistor

9-7. The *photoresistor* is a *light* sensitive resistor with resistance inversely proportional to the light. It is illustrated here.

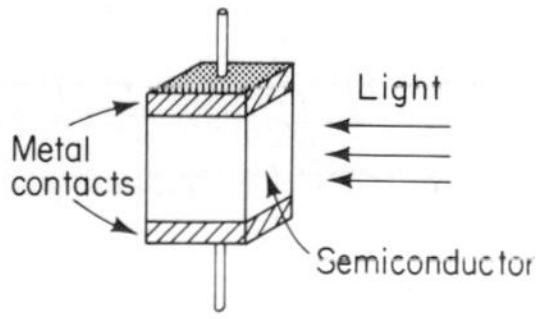

It is basically composed of two metal contacts on a photoconductive _____.

*

— — — — — — — — — — — — — —

semiconductor

9-8. The conductivity of the photoresistor *changes* as the light changes. They are manufactured in many sizes and shapes and can be found most any place that *light is used* in measuring, sensing, or control. Street lamps which automatically turn on at dusk and off at dawn could be using the _____ as the automatic _____ device.

*

— — — — — — — — — — — — — —

photoresistor
control

Varistor

9-9. The *varistor* is constructed of thyrite or silicon carbide. These have been called *nonohmic* materials. They have *maximum* resistance when voltage is steady. The resistance drops off sharply when voltage either increases or decreases. This is the voltage-resistance curve.

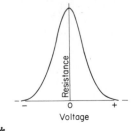

A _____ voltage produces maximum resistance. Resistance _____ rapidly as voltage changes in _____ direction.

*

— — — — — — — — — — — — — —

steady
decreases
either

392

9-10. Varistors are widely used in power supplies to protect the equipment from voltage *surges*. A surge of voltage causes a sharp _____ in resistance which effectively eliminates the _____ .

*
— — — — — — — — — — — — — —

decrease (drop)
surge

UNIQUE DIODES

9-11. *Some* P-N junction diodes have been designed to take advantage of the *adverse* characteristics of semiconductors. Characteristics which adversely affect the operation of most _____ devices are essential to the operation of some P-N _____ _____ .
*
— — — — — — — — — — — — — —

semiconductor
junction diodes

9-12. The *variable capacitance* diode is a semiconductor, P-N junction diode, but its application is that of a *voltage sensitive capacitor*. It can automatically control frequency in response to a change in bias. The variable capacitance diode is a P-N _____ diode with characteristics of a _____ _____ capacitor.
*
— __ __ __ — __ — — — — — — — — —

junction
voltage sensitive

9-13. The _____ _____ diode can be used to control _____ in response to a change in _____ .
*
— __ — __ — __ — — — — — — — — —

variable capacitance
frequency
bias

9-14. The variable capacitance diode is marketed under such *trade names* as varicaps, semicaps, and varactors. There are several trade names for the _____ _____ diode.
*
— __ __ __ — __ — — — — — — — —

variable capacitance

9-15.   The *barrier region* acts as a dielectric and causes the diode
to exhibit maximum capacitance when reverse bias first blocks
conduction.   From this point, capacitance *decreases* as reverse bias
increases.   The limits are set by the breakdown characteristics of
the diode.   The capacitance of the variable _____ diode is
_____ proportional to the quantity of _____ bias.

*

— — — — — — — — — — — — — — — —

capacitance

inversely

reverse

Symmetrical Zener Diode

9-16.   The *symmetrical zener* diode is equivalent to two ordinary
zeners placed back to back.   This is a circuit symbol and the
characteristic curve for this diode.

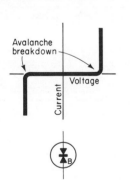

The symmetrical zener diode has *no* forward bias.
A specified voltage in *either* direction will cause
_____ breakdown.

*

— — — — — — — — — — — — — — — —

avalanche

9-17. The symmetrical zener fits into the broad category of *tunnel diodes*, but its tunneling characteristics are effective in _____ direction. This makes it a valuable _____ device for oscillators and automatic switching circuits.

*

— — — — — — — — — — — — —

either

control

Tunnel Diode

9-18. The term *tunnel diode* is properly applied to the diode invented by Dr. Leo Esaki in 1958. It is sometimes called the *Esaki diode*. This is a circuit symbol for this diode.

Collector
Emitter

The barrier is so narrow, and the barrier potential so high, that tunneling may be in effect with *zero bias*. Many diodes use a tunneling effect, but there is only one true _____ diode. Tunneling may take place in this diode with _____ bias.

*

— — — — — — — — — — — — —

tunnel

zero

9-19. Voltage is applied to this diode *only* in the forward direction.
As bias increases, current rises to a peak, and if bias continues to
increase, current will decrease. Only _____ bias is used, and
up to a point, current is _____ proportional to bias. *Above this*
point, current is _____ proportional to bias.
*

— —   — —   — —   — —   — —   — —   — —   — —   — —

forward
directly
inversely

9-20. This drawing illustrates the characteristics of the tunnel
diode.

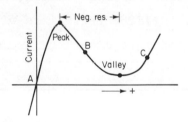

It shows that current rises _____ with
an increase in voltage until it reaches a
peak. Then it _____ as voltage
increases until it reaches a *valley*. After
passing the valley, current again _____
with an increase in voltage.

*

— —   — —   — —   — —   — —   — —   — —   — —   — —

linearly
decreases
increases

9-21. Point B is the normal *operating point*. From this point, there is a reasonable range where current varies _____ with voltage. The area from the peak to the valley is called a *negative* resistance area because resistance varies _____ with voltage.
*

— — — — — — — — — — — — — —

inversely

inversely

Silicon Rectifier

9-22. Fused junctions and heat sinks have enabled *silicon rectifier* diodes to replace most other rectifiers. Their principal asset is the ability to handle *high* current, withstand strong *reverse* voltage, and allow very *little* reverse (leakage) current. Silicon rectifiers with _____ junctions and _____ sinks have replaced most other _____ .
*

— — — — — — — — — — — — — —

fused

heat

rectifiers

9-23. This drawing illustrates two *styles* of silicon rectifier packages.

(A)   (B)

On the left, we have a _____ ____ style with a bolt for a _____ _____ .

*

plug in
heat sink

9-24. Section B of the drawing shows a *sealed* package with two _____ for solder connections.

*

leads

9-25. Silicon rectifiers can be obtained in *packages* of half-wave, full-wave, or bridge rectifiers. Voltage and current ratings seem to be no problem. *Peak inverse* voltage ratings of 15,000 volts are not rare, and they carry overage currents *up to* 1500 amperes. The _____ _____ can be obtained in any desired rectifier package with ratings for almost any value of _____ and _____ .

*

silicon rectifier
voltage
current

9-26. The silicon *controlled* rectifier (SCR) is often confused with the silicon rectifier (SR), but they bear little resemblence to one another. The silicon rectifier is a *diode* while the silicon controlled rectifier is a *four layer switch*. The SR is a _____ while the SCR is a _____ _____ _____ .

*

— — — — — — — — — — —

diode

four layer switch

9-27. This drawing illustrates the structure and a schematic symbol for the SCR.

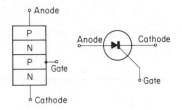

The *gate* is used to turn the switch on, and the *anode voltage* turns it off again. The switch is _____ on and the _____ voltage turns it off.

*

— — — — — — — — — — —

gated

anode

9-28. This is the *equivalent* circuit for the SCR.

It performs the same as an _____ and a _____ transistor with the output of one being the _____ to the other.

*

NPN
PNP
input

9-29. A *pulse* of current on the gate causes both transistors to *conduct*, and regenerative feedback rapidly drives them to *saturation*. The switch stays on until the *anode* voltage drops to a specified level, then it *reverts* to the off condition. The switch is turned on by a *pulse* of current to the _____ . Regenerative feedback completes the turn on by driving both transistors to _____ . Turn off is accomplished by _____ the anode voltage.

*

gate
saturation
reducing

9-30. SCRs are known by many names. The one described is commonly known as a *"gate turn off switch."* Another is *"light activated* SCR." The light activated SCR is used for automatic light dimming and light on-off control. Other SCRs may be used as amplifiers, time delays, overload protectors, light flashers, and numerous other automatic switching operations. SCRs are known by many _____ and perform a wide *variety* of _____ _____ operations.

*

— — — — — — — — — — — — — — — —

names

automatic switching

Photodiode

9-31. This is an illustration of a *photodiode.*

The _____ exposes the junction to _____ .

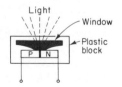

*

— — — — — — — — — — — — — — — —

window

light

9-32. The *barrier resistance* is controlled by light intensity. This
diode operates on *reverse* current. The reverse bias produces
practically no reverse current in the dark. The same bias, in the
light, produces a reverse current directly proportional to *light
intensity*. The photodiode operates on _____ current. For a
given reverse bias, the reverse current is _____ proportional
to light _____ .
*

— — — — — — — — — — — — — — — —

reverse
directly
intensity

EXTRAORDINARY TRANSISTORS

9-33. Many transistors are designed to *exploit* bothersome characteristics of semiconductors. These off-beat transistors have *extended* the
usefulness of solid state devices in areas of high power, high frequency, high speed switching, and many other special situations. Off-
beat transistors have extended the _____ of solid state devices
in many _____ situations.
*

— — — — — — — — — — — — — — — —

usefulness
special

9-34. In the past, most ordinary transistors were severely handicapped by a very *low power* capability. A 50 milliwatt transistor became known as a *power transistor*. Power of 50 milliwatts was once considered a lot of _____ for a transistor because most transistors had a very limited power _____.

*

— — — — — — — — — — — — — — — —

power
capability

9-35. Power transistors are now available which can handle *large quantities* of power. Some modern _____ transistors handle large _____ of power.

*

— — — — — — — — — — — — — — —

power
quantities

9-36. Heat *dissipation* was one difficult problem that had to be solved in order to produce a high powered transistor. The internal or external heat *ratio* is 3° to 5° C per watt of power for ordinary transistors. The power transistor needs to _____ from 3° to 5° C of heat for each _____ of power.

*

— — — — — — — — — — — — — — — —

dissipate
watt

9-37. The power transistor uses *larger* elements, more *volume* of semiconductor materials, *metal casings,* and special heat *dissipation* features. This is a drawing of one type of power transistor.

The large copper connector to the collector and the metal mounting stud are two special _____ _____ features.

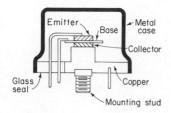

*
— — — — — — — — — — — — — — —

heat dissipation

9-38. Other methods of *carrying off* excessive heat are cooling fins, forced air, and liquid. *Cooling fins* are mounted on the metal case and provide more cooling area. *Forced air*, sometimes refrigerated, increases the rate of heat dissipation. Forced air and cooling fins are frequently combined. The *liquid* cooling system may place liquid inside the metal case or submerge the case in liquid. Cooling fins, forced air, and liquid are used to _____ excessive heat. Some- times two or more of these methods are _____ .

*
— — — — — — — — — — — — — — —

dissipate
combined

9-39. The *intrinsic* transistor is designed to minimize the collector
to base *capacitance*. This design became necessary as frequencies
increased. There comes a point in frequency when even a small
capacitor is a *direct short*. Capacitance between collector and base
was a problem which _____ as frequencies _____. The
intrinsic transistor is designed to _____ this capacitance.

*

— — — — — — — — — — — — — —

increased

increased

minimize

9-40. This is an illustration of the *structure* of an intrinsic
transistor.

The I stands for _____ material and
this is a _____ combination.

Collector N I P N Emitter
Base

*

— — — — — — — — — — — — — —

intrinsic

NIPN

9-41.   Intrinsic material is a *pure* semiconductor.   This layer of I material increases the *distance* between the plates of the collector to base capacitor.   The I material is _____ semiconductor.   Used in this manner, it _____ the distance between the capacitor _____.
*

pure

increases

plates

9-42.   The intrinsic transistor can handle frequencies up to *100 MHz*. The reduced conduction is compensated for by raising the collector voltage.   The I material decreases the _____ , decreases the _____ , and increases the operating _____ .
*

capacitance

conduction

frequencies

9-43. This drawing shows a schematic symbol and illustrates the structure of a *tetrode* transistor.

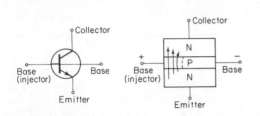

This is a _____ layer transistor with _____ external leads.

*
— — — — — — — — — — — — — — —

three

four

9-44. The *tetrode* represents a different approach to the capacitance problem. It reduces the capacitance by reducing the *size* of the plates This could be done by reducing the size of the base, but the base was already as small as feasible to produce the needed current carriers. So physical size was kept the same and *electrical size* was reduced. The tetrode design reduced the collector to base capacitance by reducing the *size* of the _____ . This was accomplished by reducing the _____ size of the transistor base.

*
— — — — — — — — — — — — — — —

plates

electrical

9-45. Two leads are attached to the base. The lead marked *"base"* has a potential only, and this potential is *cut off* reverse bias. The *injection* lead has forward bias and serves as *single input*. More than 50% of the junction stays cut off and confines electron flow to a *small area* near the injection lead. Reverse bias on the base lead holds more than _____ percent of the junction in a cut off state. Forward bias and signal on the _____ lead cause electron flow through a _____ area.

*

— — — — — — — — — — — — — —

50

injection

small

9-46. Since *only* the conducting portion of the junction produces capacitance, this action has _____ the area of both plates by more than _____ percent. This results in a much *lower* capacitance and a much *higher* frequency capability.

*

— — — — — — — — — — — — — —

reduced

50

9-47. The *field effect* transistor is another product of the effort to reduce the collector to base capacitance. This time the collector to base junction was also *eliminated*. The collector to base capacitance was the problem. Eliminating the _____ eliminates the _____ and solves the problem.

*

— — — — — — — — — — — —

junction

capacitance

9-48. This drawing illustrates the *structure* of the field effect transistor.

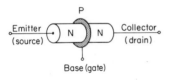

The collector and emitter are formed by one *continuous* piece of ____ type material. The base is a _____ of P type material which completely surrounds the ____ type material.

*

— — — — — — — — — — — —

N

ring

N

9-49. The base is a *doughnut* forming a continuous junction with the
N type material. The field effect transistor has _____ junction formed
between a single piece of N type material and a _____ of P type
material.

*

— — — — — — — — — — — — — — —

one

ring

9-50. This drawing illustrates the *function* of the field effect
transistor.

The electron flow is from _____ to _____ through the N type material.
The electrons *do not* pass through the _____ .

*

— — — — — — — — — — — — — — —

emitter

collector

junction

9-51. The *negative* potential on the base forms a *constrictive* electric field which repels the passing electrons. The signal is applied to the base and varies the intensity of the field. Thus, electron flow is controlled by field intensity. The signal controls the _____ intensity and the field intensity controls the flow of _____ .

*
— — — — — — — — — — — — — — — —

field

electrons

9-52. What about the *capacitance*? There *is no* electron path from base to collector. Effectively, there is no collector to base junction. Therefore, the collector to base capacitance has been _____ .

*
— — — — — — — — — — — — — — — —

eliminated

9-53. What has it done for frequency? Field effect transistors have handled frequencies in excess of *500 MHz*, and this can probably be doubled or tripled with improved designs. The field effect _____ recognizes no _____ barrier.

*
— — — — — — — — — — — — — — — —

transistor

frequency

9-54. Many situations in electronics demand a *fast* acting, *two way* switch. The *four layer* transistor is such a switch. The _____ layer transistor is a _____ acting, _____ way switch.

*
— — — — — — — — — — — — —

four

fast

two

9-55. This drawing illustrates the *structure* of the four layer transistor.

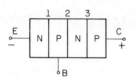

This is sometimes called a *thyristor*. It is a _____ junction transistor of the _____ variety.

*
— — — — — — — — — — — — —

three

NPNP

9-56. Junctions 1 and 3 are *forward* biased which places reverse bias on junction 2. With zero potential on the base, the current is *blocked*. There is forward bias on junctions _____ , but the reverse bias on junction ____ blocks the current.

*

— — — — — — — — — — — — —

1 and 3

2

9-57. The switch is turned on by a *positive* signal to the base. This places *forward* bias on junction 2. With all three junctions *forward* biased, the transistor leaps instantly into a condition resembling *avalanche* breakdown. It conducts at saturation, the base has no further significance, and the switch is on. The _____ signal on the base turns the switch on by driving the transistor into almost instantaneous _____ .

*

— — — — — — — — — — — — —

positive

saturation

9-58. *Removing* the signal from the base puts *reverse* bias back across junction 2, but this junction is now in a state of avalanche breakdown. Current *continues* unabated. Once the switch is on, it remains and the _____ has no control.

*

— — — — — — — — — — — — —

on

base

9-59. A specified *collector potential* is required to sustain the switch in the on position. When the *potential drops* to this level, the avalanche across junction 2 ceases and is replaced with *cut off* bias. This turns the switch *off* almost as fast as it was turned on. The switch is turned off by _____ the collector potential. When it reaches a specified level, the avalanche across junction ____ is replaced with cut off _____ .

*

— — — — — — — — — — — — —

reducing

2

bias

9-60. Here are two schematic *symbols* for the four layer transistor. This two way switch can handle *high* current and can be turned on or off in a very *short* time. The on time requires about 1/10 of a microsecond. It requires just a little longer to turn it off. The four layer transistor is a very _____ , two way _____ capable of handling _____ currents.

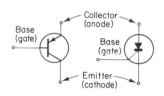

Collector
(anode)

Base
(gate)

Base
(gate)

Emitter
(cathode)

*

— — — — — — — — — — — — —

fast

switch

9-61. *Cryosars* is a coined word applied to switches which operate at *super cold* temperatures. *Cryo* means frost or icy cold, *s* means switching, *a* means avalanche, and *r* means recombination. The final s makes it plural. Cryosars means switches operating on _____ breakdown and recombination at super _____ temperatures.

*

— — — — — — — — — — — — —

avalanche
cold

9-62. The cryosar is a tiny semiconductor *switch* which operates best at −269° C. At this temperature a semiconductor has a resistance so high that it approaches *infinity*. This is the *off* condition of the cryosar. The off condition of the cryosar is an open switch with _____ resistance between the poles.

*

— — — — — — — — — — — — —

infinite

9-63. A potential as low as *one volt* can trigger the cryosar which will then reach *avalanche* breakdown in a few billionths of a second. The switch is now *on*, and there is practically *zero* resistance across it. The cryosar can be triggered by a _____ volt potential and it goes from an _____ resistance to a _____ resistance in a few billionths of a second.

*
— — — — — — — — — — — — — — — —

one

infinite

zero

9-64. The cryosar is closed again by *removing* the activating signal. This allows almost instantaneous *recombination* which stops the current with an infinite resistance. A cubic inch of space can house several thousand cryosars. The switch is opened by _____ the activating potential. This allows _____ to shut off the current with an _____ resistance.

*
— — — — — — — — — — — — — — — —

removing

recombination

infinite

9-65. The solar cell is a tiny semiconductor device which accomplishes an old old dream; it *converts* light energy directly into
usable voltage. It is estimated that *direct sunlight* delivers about
100 MW of power per square centimeter at the earth's surface. The
solar cell is about 3/4 inch in diameter and 1/4 inch thick. It
delivers about 0.5V of usable potential, and direct sunlight *is not*
a requirement. A solar cell converts _____ energy directly to
usable _____ and does so without direct _____ .

*
— — — — — — — — — — — —

light
voltage
sunlight

9-66. This drawing illustrates the *structure* of a solar cell.

The window allows _____ to contact a layer of P type _____ .

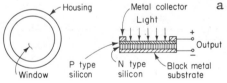
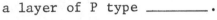

*
— — — — — — — — — — — —

light
silicon

9-67. *Under* the P type layer of silicon is a layer of N type silicon and a black metal substrate. A metal *collector ring* is in contact with the P type material. The light causes a *difference in potential* across the P-N junction which is reflected in the metal contacts. This potential is delivered to the output as a *usable* voltage. The light establishes a difference in _____ across the junction. This is delivered to the output as usable _____ .
*

— — — — — — — — — — — — — — —

potential

voltage

9-68. This device is *effective* in light 1/10,000 the strength of direct sunlight. Voltage is directly proportional to light intensity up to a certain *critical point*. After that, voltage holds constant. In weak light, _____ is _____ proportional to light intensity After a critical _____ is reached voltage holds constant.
*

— — — — — — — — — — — — — — —

voltage

directly

intensity

9-69. Many thousands of solar cells have been used to power equipment on manned space flights, space probes, and satellites. The most interesting thing about a solar cell is its *life expectancy*. Barring physical damage, a cell can be expected to perform satisfactorily for several thousand years. Solar cells are small, light weight, and have a _____ life expectancy. They have been used successfully to power equipment of _____ flights.

*
— — — — — — — — — — — —

long

space

OUTSTANDING AMPLIFIERS

9-70. When frequencies reached the *30 GHz range* ($G=10^9$) noise and transit time became two very serious *problems*. Trying to find amplifiers that could solve these problems led to a breakthrough in electronic science. A breakthrough in electronic science came as a direct result of trying to construct _____ for 30 GHz frequencies that could solve the problems of _____ and _____ time.

*
— — — — — — — — — — — —

amplifiers

noise

transit

9-71. The maser amplifier was built by the Columbia University in
1957. This is an acronym from words describing the *operation*:
"microwave amplification by stimulated emission of radiation." The
maser *eliminates* the need for electron flow which neatly *bypasses*
the problems of noise generation and transit time. The maser
solves both _____ and _____ time problems by eliminating the need
for _____ flow.
*

— — — — — — — — — — — — — — — —

noise

transit

electron

9-72. Radiation is *stimulated* by raising the normal energy level of
a group of atoms. One method of doing this is to place the atoms in
a strong magnetic field and bombard them with waves of RF energy.
Whatever method used to raise the energy level is known as a process
of *pumping or population inversion*. Pumping is a process of _____
the energy level of a group of _____.
*

— — — — — — — — — — — — — — — —

raising

atoms

9-73. The *microwave signal* to be amplified is passed through the confined group of high energy atoms. As the signal passes, the atoms are *triggered* back to their normal energy level. In doing so, each atom *radiates* a quantity of energy which is absorbed by the signal. The signal is _____ by passing through the high _____ atoms. The atoms _____ energy which is absorbed by the signal.

*

— — — — — — — — — — — — — —

amplified
energy
radiate

9-74. The radiated energy is released *in phase* with the triggering signal so that the energy released from the atoms is transferred to the signal. The signal *absorbs* more energy as it moves and its amplitude *grows* larger in the process. The triggering _____ causes the atoms to release energy which _____ to the signal. As the signal absorbs energy its amplitude grows _____ .

*

— — — — — — — — — — — — — —

signal
transfers
larger

9-75. The pumping frequency *energizes* the atoms; the triggering signal *releases and absorbs* the energy and is amplified in the process. One signal imparts energy to the _____ . Another signal _____ and _____ this energy.

*

— — — — — — — — — — — — — —

atoms
releases
absorbs

9-76. The radiating *material* for a maser may be either gas or a crystal of solid state material. *Among many* materials used successfully are ammonia gas and ruby crystals. A maser may use either _____ or _____ material for radiation. _____ crystals are used and so is _____ gas.

*

— — — — — — — — — — — — —

gas

semiconductor

ruby

ammonia

9-77. This drawing illustrates the *functional parts* of a ruby rod maser.

The functional parts are a pump frequency *resonator*, a *coil*, a _____ rod, and an output _____ .

*

— — — — — — — — — — — — —

ruby

resonator

9-78. The coil is wound *around* the pump frequency resonator, and the dc potential *energizes* the coil. A strong magnetic field is *concentrated* in the center of the resonator. The _____ coil concentrates the magnetic _____ at the _____ of the resonator.

*

— — — — — — — — — — — — — — —

dc

field

center

9-79. Both resonators are simply *hollow* cylinders, but when the proper frequency is applied, they react as a *tuned tank* circuit. The output resonator is *smaller* because it resonates to the *higher* signal frequency. Resonators are _____ cylinders, but they are electrically tuned ____ _____ to the proper frequency.

*

— — — — — — — — — — — — — — —

hollow

tank circuits

9-80. The *ruby rod* is threaded through the pump resonator at the point of *maximum* magnetic flux. It passes all the way through this resonator and into the output resonator. The ruby rod passes through the _____ _____ at a point of maximum _____ concentration.

*

— — — — — — — — — — — — — — —

pump resonator

flux (field)

9-81. The pump signal causes *resonance* inside the cavity. The circulating pump signal and the magnetic field *transfer energy* to the atoms in the ruby rod. The pump signal causes the cavity to

_____. Energy from this action and the magnetic field transfers to the _____ in the ruby rod.

*

—— —— —— —— —— —— —— —— —— —— —— —— ——

resonate

atoms

9-82. The *triggering* signal is the signal to be amplified. It is coupled *directly* into the end of the ruby rod. As the signal passes down the length of the rod, it *absorbs* energy from the energized atoms. It *grows* in amplitude as it moves so that each sine wave of the signal is larger than the one following it. The triggering signal moves through the _____ _____ and absorbs energy from the energized _____ . The signal is _____ as it moves.

*

—— —— —— —— —— —— —— —— —— —— —— —— ——

ruby rod

atoms

amplified

9-83. The greatly amplified signal couples from the ruby rod *directly* into the output resonator. The signal causes *resonance* in this cavity and enables coupling to an output circuit without loss of energy. Amplified _____ from the ruby rod cause _____ in the output resonator. Signals can be coupled from the resonator without loss of _____.
*

— — — — — — — — — — — — —

signals

resonance

energy

9-84. The drawing seems to indicate that the input and output are carried on *ordinary wires*. This *is not* the case. These are micro-wave frequencies, and they are coupled through *wave guides*. The signal being amplified is a _____ frequency and coupling is accomplished by use of _____ _____.
*

— — — — — — — — — — — — —

microwave

wave guides

9-85. Efforts to increase the operating frequency of the maser led
to the discovery that *light wave* frequencies could be amplified.
The light amplifier was called a *laser*.   The *first* laser was
developed by the Hughes Aircraft Company in July 1960.   This was
closely followed by a similar development by the Bell Laboratories.
Then many companies were developing lasers.   The laser is a _____
amplifier which was developed in an effort to improve the microwave
_____ .

*
— — — — — — — — — — — — —

light
maser

9-86.   The word laser was *coined* from "light amplification by stimulated emission of radiation."   There is no sharp *dividing line*
between the maser and the laser.   The basic difference is the frequencies handled.   In fact, the laser has been called a light maser.
The laser amplifies _____ in much the same manner that the maser
amplifies _____ .
*
— — — — — — — — — — — — —

light
microwaves

9-87. Lasers raised the electronic frequency *spectrum* all the way through the *visible light* frequencies and opened up a new frontier for electronic expansion. With lasers, all visible light _____ are now in the electronic _____ _____ .

*
— — — — — — — — — — — — —

frequencies
frequency spectrum

9-88. Lasers of *many applications* are now in use with others being developed at a rapid pace. They hold *great promise* for communications, industrial applications, and medical use. Lasers have many _____ , and improvement in communications is sure to result.

*
— — — — — — — — — — — — —

applications

9-89. A laser beam with *10 joules* of power (1 joule = 1 watt - second) can burn wood and paper over a distance of *one mile*. The same beam can *carry intelligence* over a distance of *10 million miles* and be detected by a three inch lens. A low powered laser can carry _____ over fantastic distances.

*
— — — — — — — — — — — — —

intelligence

9-90. It has been proven that *tremendous quantities* of information can be modulated into a single laser beam. All the information carried by *seven* television channels (audio, video, color, and black and white) has been carried *simultaneously* on a single pencil size beam of light. Large _____ of information can be carried on a single _____ of light.

*
— — — — — — — — — — — — —

quantities

beam

SUMMARY

1. A *thermistor* is a solid state resistor with resistance inversely proportional to temperature.

2. The indirectly heated thermistor can maintain a *constant resistance* despite changes in temperature.

3. The *photoresistor* has a resistance inversely proportional to the incident light.

4. *Varistors* are constructed of nonohmic materials such as thyrite or silicon carbide.

5. A varistor has maximum resistance when a *steady voltage* is applied.

6. The *variable capacitance diode* is widely used as a voltage sensitive capacitor.

7. The *capacitance* of a variable capacitance diode is maximum with application of barely cut off bias. This capacitance decreases as reverse bias increases.

8. The *symmetrical zener* diode is similar to two ordinary zeners connected back to back. It operates at avalanche breakdown in either direction.

9. When carriers appear to pass through a barrier region, this is known as the *zener effect,* avalanche breakdown, or tunneling.

10. The *tunnel diode* has two areas where current is directly proportional to voltage. It also has one extensive *negative resistance* area where current varies inversely with voltage.

11. Varieties of *silicon rectifiers* are available to suit most rectifier needs. They can be obtained with high current and voltage
ratings.

12. The internal to external *heat difference* in a transistor is from
3°to 5° C per watt of power. Power transistors have rugged,
larger elements and special ways to dissipate the heat.

13. The effort to reduce the collector to base capacitance of transistors led to the development of the *intrinsic transistor,* the
tetrode transistor, and the *field effect transistor*.

14. The intrinsic transistor has a smaller collector to base capacitance because the capacitor plates are farther apart. The
tetrode transistor accomplishes the same thing by having electrically smaller capacitor plates. In the *field effect* transistor,
the capacitance has been eliminated by eliminating the current
path from base to collector.

15. The *four layer* transistor is a high speed, two way switch.

16. The *gated switch,* silicon control rectifier operates similar to
the four layer transistor.

17. The *photodiode* operates on reverse current, and the reverse
current for a given bias is directly proportional to the light
intensity.

18. *Cryosars* are tiny, semiconductor switches operated at super cold
temperatures. The switch can be turned on and off by applying
and removing a small activating voltage.

19. The *open* cryosar has almost *infinite* resistance; the *closed*
cryosar has practically *zero* resistance.

20. The *solar cell* is a small semiconductor device which converts
light energy directly to usable voltage.

21. The *maser* was developed in an effort to overcome the problems of
noise and transit time at microwave frequencies.

22. The maser amplifies these microwave frequencies by raising the
energy level of a group of atoms when *triggering* them back to
their normal energy level. The triggering signal absorbs the
released energy and is amplified in the process.

23. High frequency masers led to the development of the *laser* which
is a light amplifier.

24. *Large quantities* of information can be carried by a single, low
powered laser beam.

25. Lasers have moved the electronic frequency *spectrum* up to the
top of the *visible light* frequencies.

Conclusion

This concludes the program and a section of review exercises follows.

SECTION 10
REVIEW EXERCISES

This section contains a review *exercise for each* of the preceding sections. These exercises are intended to reinforce learning *after* you have completed the program. They should be completed as *often* as you like to check your *retention* of the material. Several incorrect responses in any given exercise *indicate* that a review of the corresponding section is in order for maximum retention. The correct responses to each exercise appear immediately after the exercise for *ease* of verification.

EXERCISE FOR SECTION 1
Electron Tubes

1. Most electron tubes are based on the principle of _____ emission which is known as the _____ .

2. The Edison effect is a process of releasing _____ by applying _____ to a metal.

3. The direction of electron current is from _____ to _____ in the external circuit.

4. Current is measured in _____ , and one unit of current is _____ electrons passing a point in one second.

5. The first electron tube was a _____ . It was called a _____ after its inventer.

6. The first diode consisted of a _____ , a _____ , and a glass envelope.

7. In electron emission, electrons break away from the _____ and escape into _____ .

8. A thin restraining wall on the surface of metals which prevents free escape of electrons is called the _____ .

9. The quantity of work required to free an electron from a piece of metal is the _____ of that particular metal.

10. Edison's experiment as well as the first diode demonstrated the _____ type of emission.

11. Secondary emission results from _____ electrons bombarding a _____ surface.

12. When electrons are ripped away from a surface by strong electric fields, this is _____ emission.

13. Photoemission results when _____ strikes a photosensitive material.

14. Of the four principal types of emission, how many types are used in electron tubes? Which type is the most popular?

15. Strontium-coated nickel alloy is frequently used as an emitter. It is a compromise between the best _____ and the _____ material.

16. The two requirements for current through a diode are a _____ emitter and a plate potential more _____ than the cathode.

17. The space charge is a cloud of _____ between the _____ and _____ of a tube.

18. A tube is saturated when the _____ is exhausted because the plate is using all the available _____ .

19. The formula for dc plate resistance is _____ .

20. When a change of 6 volts on the plate produces a change of 5 mA in plate current, the diode has an ac plate resistance of _____ ohms.

21. The diodes' principal use is _____ .

22. The active elements of a triode are _____ , plate, and _____ .

23. All potentials on the electron tube are with respect to the _____ . Bias is a _____ voltage on the _____ _____ .

24. The capabilities of a triode are revealed by charts known as _____ .

25. Name three important tube constants.

26. Amplification is a ratio of _____ voltage to _____ voltage. It is called gain and is a number expressing the effectiveness of the _____ in controlling plate current.

27. The formula for amplification factor is _____ .

28. Transconductance is measured in _____ , and the formula is _____ .

29. When signals are coupled into the grid and out from the plate, they will be _____ and _____ .

30. The principal use of a cathode ray tube is to _____ information.

31. There are two common types of CRTs; they are _____ and _____ .

32. All CRTs contain one or more electron guns. The gun fires a _____ of electrons toward a _____ .

33. The electrostatic CRT traces patterns by varying the _____ on the deflection _____ .

34. The aquadag coating _____ the electrons and _____ them to the power supply.

Responses to Section 1 Exercise

(1) Thermionic; Edison effect. (2) Electrons; heat. (3) Negative; positive. (4) Amperes; 6.24×10^{18}. (5) Diode; Fleming valve. (6) Filament; plate. (7) Material; space. (8) Surface barrier. (9) Work function. (10) Thermionic. (11) Primary; metallic. (12) Field. (13) Light. (14) All four; Thermionic. (15) Emitter; strongest. (16) Heated; positive. (17) Electrons; plate; cathode. (18) Space charge; electrons. (19) $R_p = E_p/I_p$. (20) 1200. (21) Rectification. (22) Cathode; control grid. (23) Cathode; negative; control grid. (24) Characteristic curves. (25) Amplification factor, transconductance, and ac plate resistance. (26) Input; output; grid. (27) $\mu = \Delta e_p/\Delta e_g$. (28) Mhos; $g_m = \Delta i_p/\Delta e_p$. (29) Amplified; inverted. (30) Display. (31) Electrostatic; electromagnetic. (32) Beam; screen. (33) Potential; plates. (34) Collects; returns.

EXERCISE FOR SECTION 2
Solid State Devices

1. A material which is neither a good insulator nor a good conductor is a _____ .

2. A natural atom has the same number of _____ in orbit as it has _____ in the nucleus.

3. Electron paths are _____ bands or shells. _____ shells is the largest number in any atom.

4. The outer band is the _____ band, and it may contain a maximum of _____ electrons.

5. An atom with eight valence electrons has a _____ valence band. It is a chemically _____ atom.

6. If the valence band contains less than four electrons, the material is a good _____ because the atoms readily _____ their valence electrons.

7. If the valence band contains more than four electrons, the atoms _____ other electrons.

8. A trivalent material _____ electrons while a pentavalent material _____ other electrons.

9. Good semiconductor materials have valence bands about _____ _____ and are formed into _____ lattice structures.

10. The crystal lattice is formed by atoms _____ their valence electrons in covalent _____ .

11. The absence of an electron in a covalent bond constitutes a _____ which is equivalent to a small _____ charge.

12. Both holes and electrons contribute to electron movement and are called _____ . The hole is a _____ , and the electron is a _____ .

13. Doping is a process of mixing materials to produce crystals which contain either an excess of _____ or an excess of _____ .

14. A donor material is a material with an excess of _____ . An acceptor material has an excess of _____ .

15. A diode is created by forming a _____ junction between P and N type materials.

16. The area near the junction has no _____ and is called the _____ .

17. Junctions can be grown by varying the _____ of a melt.

18. Voltage on a diode is called bias. If it aids the majority carriers, it is _____ bias. If it aids the minority carriers, it is _____ bias.

19. Reverse bias over a critical amount will result in _____ . Some diodes operate in the _____ region.

20. When a diode is used as a positive rectifier, it passes the _____ alternations and eliminates the _____ alternations.

21. The zener diode is designed to operate in the _____ region.

22. A transistor has two or more P-N _____ . The triode is equivalent to two _____ .

23. The three elements of a triode are _____ , _____ , and _____ .

24. The two types of triodes are _____ and _____ .

25. The base of a transistor is a thin slice of either P or N type material _____ two pieces of the _____ type material.

26. In the schematic symbol, the element with the arrow is the _____ , and the arrow points _____ to the direction of current.

27. The direction of the arrow also identifies the type of transistor because it points toward _____ type material.

28. For proper operation, the input junction of a transistor is _____ biased, and the output junction is _____ biased.

29. In either type of transistor, the _____ current is the total current.

30. In the NPN, current _____ through the emitter and divides between base and collector. The base receives about _____ percent of the total current and the remaining _____ percent leaves through the collector.

31. In the PNP, current _____ through the base and collector. About _____ percent comes through the base and the other _____ percent through the collector. This total current leaves through the _____ .

32. A small signal across the _____ junction causes a large change across the _____ junction.

33. A small signal can overdrive a transistor and cause either cut off or saturation (sometimes both). Overdriving results in _____ _____ .

34. Transistors are commonly used for both _____ and electronic _____ .

Responses for Section 2 Exercise

(1) Semiconductor. (2) Electrons; protons. (3) Energy; Seven.
(4) Valence; eight. (5) Full; stable. (6) Conductor; release.
(7) Attract. (8) Releases; attracts. (9) Half full; crystal.
(10) Sharing; bonding. (11) Hole; positive. (12) Current carriers;
positive carrier; negative carrier. (13) Electrons; holes.
(14) Electrons; holes. (15) Chemical. (16) Carriers; depletion
region. (17) Temperature. (18) Forward; reverse. (19) Breakdown;
breakdown. (20) Positive; negative. (21) Breakdown.
(22) Junctions; diodes. (23) Base, emitter, and collector.
(24) NPN; PNP. (25) Between; opposite. (26) Emitter; opposite.
(27) N. (28) Forward; reverse. (29) Emitter. (30) Enters; 2;
98. (31) Enters; 2; 98; emitter. (32) Input; output. (33) Amplitude distortion. (34) Amplifiers; switches.

EXERCISE FOR SECTION 3
Power Conversion

1. Over the years, the most practical sources of electric energy
   have been the _____ and the _____ .

2. Most power systems require some type of _____ unit in order to
   provide the proper voltage.

3. The dynamotor changes dc to either a _____ or a
   _____ .

4. The rotary converter is a combination ac _____ and dc _____
   _____ .

5. The inverter changes _____ to _____ .

6. There are two types of vibrators. One type increases the
   _____ of dc. The other type changes _____ to _____ .

7. Generators are designed to provide one, _____ , or _____
   phase outputs.

8. A well-balanced, three phase generator may use a minimum of
   _____ input lines and _____ output lines.

9. The first component after the power cord in most equipment is a
   _____ .

10. Energy through a transformer is _____ coupled from _____ to _____ .

11. The power transformer uses iron alloy cores to increase the _____ .

12. The iron cores are laminated to reduce _____ .

13. The relationship between input and output of a transformer is determined by the input to output _____ .

14. A step-up transformer has more turns on the _____ than it has on the _____ .

15. When voltage is stepped up, current is _____ by the same ratio.

16. The ideal transformer has the same power in both _____ and _____ .

17. Suppose that we have an ideal transformer with 50 turns on the primary and 200 turns on the secondary. With an E_p of 50 volts and an I_p of 16 amperes, what are the values of secondary voltage and current?

18. Impedance couples both ways through a transformer; therefore, the impedance ratio is _____ proportional to the _____ of the turns ratio.

19. What turns ratio does a transformer need in order to match a 50 ohm circuit to a 600 ohm circuit?

20. A practical transformer has three kinds of losses; they are _____ loss, _____ loss, and _____ loss.

21. Transformer efficiency is _____ divided by _____ .

22. Power transformers are designed for one specific frequency in the frequency range from _____ Hz to _____ Hz.

23. Rectification changes _____ to _____ .

24. The half-wave rectifier passes one _____ for each period of the input.

25. The average voltage from a half-wave rectifier with a 100 volt peak input is _____ volts.

26. The full-wave rectifier passes both _____ of the input sine wave.

27. The bridge rectifier produces _____ wave rectification with _____ current.

28. Three phase power requires three phase _____ , _____ , and _____ .

29. Half-wave rectifiers are best suited for _____ voltage and _____ current.

30. Full-wave rectifiers can deliver _____ voltage and reasonably _____ current.

Responses for Section 3 Exercise

(1) Battery; generator. (2) Conversion. (3) Higher dc; lower dc. (4) Motor; generator. (5) dc; ac. (6) Amplitude; dc; ac. (7) Two; three. (8) Three; three. (9) Transformer. (10) Magnetically; primary; secondary. (11) Coupling efficiency. (12) Eddy currents. (13) Turns ratio. (14) Secondary; primary. (15) Stepped down. (16) Primary; secondary. (17) 200 volts; 4 amperes. (18) Directly; square. (19) 1:4 step up. (20) Copper; hysteresis; eddy current. (21) Power out; power in. (22) 60; 1600. (23) ac; pulsating dc. (24) Alternation. (25) 31.85. (26) Alternations. (27) Full; high. (28) Generators, transformers, and rectifiers. (29) High; low. (30) Low; high.

EXERCISE FOR SECTION 4
Voltage Control

1. When the rectifier output is not of the proper amplitude, it can be corrected by using either _____ units or _____ .

2. The voltage multiplier _____ the amplitude of _____ voltage.

3. A single stage of voltage multiplication can multiply the input by a factor of _____ , _____ , or _____ .

4. When voltage doublers furnish outputs in excess of 10 kV, the voltage is _____ among several _____ .

5. The cascade voltage doubler can be changed to a tripler or a quadrupler by adding _____ .

6. Filtering is a process of reducing the _____ of a pulsating dc.

7. The capacitive input, RC filter consists of a capacitor and a _____ connected in _____ .

8. In capacitor input, RC filters, when the rectifier conducts the capacitor _____ . During cut off time, the capacitor is _____ through the resistor.

9. The RC, capacitor input filter is good for supplying _____ voltage and _____ current.

10. Effectiveness of capacitor input filters decreases as _____ increases. The _____ input is more suited for appreciable levels of _____ .

11. The best filter for high currents and changing loads is composed of two _____ type, _____ input filters.

12. The main purpose of a bleeder resistor is to _____ the filter when power is removed.

13. A secondary purpose of the bleeder is to keep a minimal _____ through the filter when the _____ is removed.

14. The voltage regulator is intended to prevent _____ in dc voltage.

15. The simplest form of shunt regulator is a variable resistor in _____ with the load.

16. Voltage level can be affected by an increase or decrease in load _____ and by an increase or decrease in input _____ .

17. The zener diode shunt regulator compensates for a voltage change by varying the _____ current and changing the _____ along the input line.

18. Shunt regulators waste energy because the _____ current bypasses the _____ .

19. The simplest form of series voltage regulator is a variable resistor in _____ with the   .

20. The series regulator compensates for voltage changes by _____ the voltage drop across the _____ .

21. The electronic series regulator automatically _____ changes and _____ for them.

22. The electronic series regulator uses a _____ as the automatically variable resistor.

23. When voltage is regulated, the _____ is automatically regulate at the same time.

24. A thermistor in series with a _____ makes a good _____ regulator.

Responses for Section 4 Exercise

(1) Conversion; electronic circuits. (2) Increases; dc. (3) Two, three, or four. (4) Divided; capacitors. (5) RC sections. (6) ac ripple. (7) Resistor; parallel. (8) Charges; discharging. (9) High; low. (10) Current; choke; current. (11) L; choke. (12) Discharge. (13) Current; load. (14) Variations. (15) Parallel. (16) Current; voltage. (17) Shunt (zener); voltage. (18) Shunt; load. (19) Series; load. (20) Varying; series resistor. (21) Detects; compensates. (22) Transistor. (23) Current. (24) Resistor; shunt.

EXERCISE FOR SECTION 5
Amplification

1. Amplification is a process which _____ the magnitude of a signal.

2. Amplifiers are designed to amplify one or more components of a signal. There are _____ , _____ , and _____ amplifiers.

3. For proper operating bias, the NPN has the emitter _____ with respect to the base and the collector _____ with respect to the base.

4. When the PNP is properly biased, the emitter is _____ with respect to the base and the collector is _____ with respect to the base.

5. The input junction _____ is varied by the input signal. The amount of variation is equivalent to the _____ value of the signal.

6. When the input signal is too large, amplitude distortion may be caused from both _____ and _____ limiting.

7. A voltage gain of 60 indicates that the output voltage has an amplitude equivalent to _____ times the input amplitude.

8. For each three dB of power gain, the output power is either _____ or _____ .

9. When a 1 μA change of input produces a 2 mA change of output, the current gain is _____ .

10. The class of amplifier indicates the _____ of the amplifier.

11. For high fidelity amplification, class _____ is used.

12. The amplifier configurations are named according to the _____ that is common to both _____ and _____ .

13. Static characteristic curves are provided for the common _____ and common _____ configurations.

14. The maximum current gain in the common base is referred to as _____ , and the formula is _____ .

15. The maximum current gain in the common emitter is referred to as _____ , and the formula is _____ .

16. The common collector is characterized by _____ input resistance, _____ output resistance, and a voltage gain less than _____ .

17. Maximum current gain in the common collector is a small change of _____ divided by a small change of _____ .

18. The load line indicates how a transistor will perform in a _____ circuit.

19. The load line connects all the possible values of collector _____ , collector _____ , and base _____ for a particular circuit.

20. The operating point indicates the circuit conditions in the _____ of an input.

21. When the operating point is too high or too low on the dynamic characteristic transfer curve, a _____ output will result from the _____ conduction.

22. The constant power line connects all points where voltage times _____ is equal to the _____ .

23. A sine wave can be converted to a _____ by over-driving an amplifier.

24. Self-biasing a transistor improves the _____ stability.

25. The four common types of coupling are direct, RC, _____ , and _____ .

26. The type of coupling is probably dictated by the signal _____ _____ .

27. The most flexible type of coupling is _____ .

28. Link coupling is a special application of _____ coupling.

29. The portion of the output signal which couples back to the input is _____ .

30. Types of amplifiers indicate the band of _____ they are designed for.

31. The video amplifier should handle frequencies from _____ to _____ MHz.

32. A square wave is composed of a _____ frequency and an infinite number of _____ .

33. A video signal with a distorted leading edge indicates improper amplification of the _____ components.

34. Degenerative (negative) feedback _____ the input signal.

35. Cross over distortion in a push-pull amplifier can be eliminated by _____ both transistors.

Responses for Section 5 Exercise

(1) Increases. (2) Voltage, current, and power. (3) Negative; positive. (4) Positive; negative. (5) Bias; peak. (6) Cut off; saturation. (7) 60. (8) Doubled; halved. (9) 2000. (10) Conduction time. (11) A. (12) Element; input; output. (13) Base; emitter. (14) Alpha; $\alpha = \Delta I_c / \Delta I_e$. (15) Beta; $\beta = \Delta I_c / \Delta I_b$. (16) Low; high; unity. (17) I_e; I_b. (18) Particular. (19) Voltage, current; current. (20) Absence. (21) Distorted; nonlinear. (22) Current; rated power. (23) Square wave. (24) Thermal. (25) Impedance; transformer. (26) Frequency. (27) Transformer. (28) Transformer. (29) Feedback. (30) Frequencies. (31) 0; 4. (32) Fundamental; odd harmonics. (33) High frequency. (34) Opposes. (35) Forward biasing.

EXERCISE FOR SECTION 6
Signal Generation and Control

1. A circuit which is designed to control the maximum _____ of a signal is a limiter.

2. Any part of the signal can be eliminated by placing the proper _____ on a limiter.

3. A transistor may perform amplification, and at the same time, serve as both a _____ and a _____ limiter.

4. The clamper is designed to establish the dc _____ for a signal.

5. A sweep generator is a circuit which produces a _____ wave shape.

6. A sweep generator can be constructed from a voltage sensitive switch and a _____ .

7. Among the many ways to produce a square wave, one of the most popular is the use of a _____ .

8. A free running multivibrator determines its own _____ and produces a series of _____ .

9. In a synchronized multivibrator, there is an input signal to start every _____ of the output.

10. The bistable multivibrator must have a _____ to initiate every _____ action.

11. The monostable multivibrator must be triggered into the _____ condition and will revert automatically to the _____ condition.

12. A nonrotating device which produces and maintains fluctuations at a predetermined frequency is an _____ .

13. Resonant circuits require periodic injections of energy in order to sustain _____ .

14. The frequency of a crystal is determined by its _____ .

15. The crystal oscillates at a highly _____ frequency.

16. The magnetostrictive effect of iron can be used to control oscillator _____ .

17. Any amplifier which has sufficient _____ will become an oscillator.

18. A synchronized blocking oscillator conducts briefly each time it is _____ and produces a _____ wave shape in its output.

19. A frequency multiplier is an oscillator tuned to some _____ of the input frequency.

20. In frequency multipliers, _____ and _____ are very common.

21. All counters are frequency _____ because they produce an output after a specified number of inputs.

22. The accuracy of a frequency divider depends upon inputs that are of a constant _____ and _____ .

23. Modulation is a process of impressing _____ upon a _____ wave.

24. The type of modulation which keys the carrier on and off is _____ modulation.

25. Amplitude modulation causes the carrier _____ to vary at an _____ rate.

26. The microphone changes sound waves into _____ signals.

27. In frequency modulation, the _____ of the carrier is caused to vary at an _____ rate.

28. Amplitude modulation is accomplished by controlling the _____ of the final RF _____ .

29. Frequency modulation is accomplished by controlling the _____ of the RF _____ .

30. Demodulation is the process of _____ intelligence from a _____ .

31. Demodulation is accomplished primarily through _____ and _____ .

32. The process of mixing two frequencies and extracting the difference frequency is _____ .

33. Detection is a process of _____ and _____ .

34. A converter combines the functions of a _____ and a _____ .

35. A frequency discriminator provides an output with an _____ directly proportional to the input _____ .

Responses for Section 6 Exercise

(1) Amplitude. (2) Bias. (3) Positive; negative. (4) Starting point. (5) Sawtooth. (6) RC network. (7) Multivibrator. (8) Frequency; square waves. (9) Alternation. (10) Trigger; switching. (11) Unstable; stable. (12) Oscillator. (13) Oscillations. (14) Thickness. (15) Stable. (16) Frequencies. (17) Regenerative feedback. (18) Triggered; pulse. (19) Harmonic. (20) Doublers; triplers. (21) Dividers. (22) Amplitude; duration.

(23) Intelligence; carrier. (24) Continuous wave. (25) Amplitude; audio. (26) Electric audio. (27) Frequency; audio. (28) Gain; amplifier. (29) Frequency; oscillator. (30) Extracting; carrier wave. (31) Heterodyning; detection. (32) Heterodyning. (33) Rectifying; filtering. (34) Mixer; local oscillator. (35) Amplitude; frequency.

EXERCISE FOR SECTION 7
Transmission and Reception

1. The transmitter generates, _____ , amplifies, and _____ electromagnetic carrier waves.

2. The transmitter type corresponds to the type of _____ used.

3. In all transmitters, the basic carrier frequency is produced by the _____ .

4. The frequency of the basic carrier may be increased through several stages of _____ before it is transmitted.

5. In amplitude modulation, the final RF amplifier receives a _____ wave input and a _____ wave input.

6. The audio signal varies the _____ on the amplifier and causes _____ variations in the output carrier.

7. The amplitude-modulated carrier contains a center frequency and two _____ .

8. The center frequency plus the audio frequency is the _____ _____ .

9. The center frequency minus the audio frequency is the _____ _____ .

10. The AM band width is measured from the _____ side band frequency to the _____ side band frequency.

11. In AM, the degree of modulation is a ratio between the voltage amplitude of the _____ signal and the _____ wave.

12. When an AM signal remains at zero amplitude for a finite period of time, _____ modulation is being used and undesirable frequencies will be _____ .

13. In the FM, the rest frequency is the oscillator frequency when there is no _____ frequency.

14. The oscillator in the FM transmitter has its frequency altered by the _____ input and the feedback from the _____ circuit.

15. The preemphasis network improves the signal to noise ratio by increasing the _____ of the _____ frequency audio signals.

16. In FM, a low frequency audio causes a _____ change in oscillator frequency; a high frequency audio causes a _____ change in oscillator frequency.

17. In FM, a low amplitude audio causes a _____ shift from center frequency; a high amplitude audio causes a _____ shift from center frequency.

18. In FM, there are many side bands. The significant side bands are those which have an amplitude as much as _____ percent of the _____ amplitude.

19. The single side band transmitter suppresses the audio frequency, the _____ frequency, and one of the _____ frequencies.

20. The SSB transmitter can concentrate more _____ on the frequencies being transmitted, and it allows more _____ in a given frequency spectrum.

21. The receiver types match the _____ types.

22. Most AM receivers are of the _____ type.

23. Three stages in the AM receiver are tuned by the selection control. These are the _____ , _____ , and _____ .

24. After passing the mixer stage, the amplitude modulation is carried by the _____ .

25. Double conversion indicates that the receiver uses two _____ , two _____ , and two _____ frequencies.

26. The AGC is intended to prevent signal fading by producing an overall signal gain which is _____ proportional to the average _____ .

27. In FM receivers, the deemphasis network provides a gain that is _____ proportional to audio _____ .

28. In single side band receivers, the carrier reinsertion oscillator produces a continuous RF which is equivalent to the missing _____ .

(1) Modulates; radiates. (2) Modulation. (3) RF oscillator.
(4) Frequency multiplication. (5) Carrier; modulation. (6) Bias;
amplitude. (7) Side bands. (8) Upper side band. (9) Lower side
band. (10) Lowest; highest. (11) Modulating; carrier. (12) Over;
generated. (13) Modulating. (14) Audio; AFC. (15) Amplitude;
high. (16) Slow; rapid. (17) Small; wide. (18) One; carrier.
(19) Carrier; side band. (20) Power; channels. (21) Transmitter.
(22) Superheterodyne. (23) RF amplifier, mixer, and local oscillator. (24) Intermediate frequency. (25) Mixers; local oscillators;
intermediate. (26) Directly; signal strength. (27) Inversely;
frequency. (28) Carrier frequency.

EXERCISE FOR SECTION 8
Transmission Lines and Antennas

1. The open wire transmission line should have uniform spacing of no
   more than _____ of a wave length.

2. Placing the open line near metallic objects increases the _____
   _____ loss.

3. The stranded wire ribbon is a good transmission line for
   _____ applications.

4. The two transmission lines that are relatively immune to their
   environments are the _____ line and _____ line.

5. Microwave frequencies use _____ as transmission lines

6. Each transmission line has its own limits for _____ and
   _____ .

7. The transmission line couples the signal from its _____ to its
   _____ .

8. In the transmitter, the signal source is the final _____
   _____ and the load is the _____ .

9. In the receiver, the signal source is the _____ and the load is
   the first _____ .

10. The characteristic impedance of a transmission line is equivalent
    _____ or _____ .

11. A nonresonant line terminated in its characteristic impedance has the same characteristics as an _____ line.

12. In a properly terminated, nonresonant line nearly all of the energy is _____ to and _____ by the load.

13. An energized line has an _____ between the conductors, and each conductor is surrounded by a _____ .

14. The E lines are from _____ to _____ , and the H lines are _____ to the E lines.

15. The field propagation rate is determined by the propagation _____ and the signal _____ .

16. During each period of a frequency, a signal will propagate a distance of one _____ for that medium.

17. In space, all electromagnetic waves propagate _____ per second which is equivalent to one _____ per period for any given frequency.

18. The velocity of propagation constant is a percentage which compares velocity in a _____ with the velocity in _____ .

19. The signal travels as a wave front along the line from the _____ to the _____ .

20. When a transmission line *is not* terminated in Z_o, it is a _____ line.

21. A resonant line has standing waves as a result of _____ energy.

22. The open end of a line is equivalent to a _____ circuit.

23. The shorted end of a line is equivalent to a _____ circuit.

24. Odd quarter wave lengths from an open are a _____ ; even quarter wave lengths from an open are a _____ .

25. For distances other than exact multiples of quarter-wave lengths in a resonant line, the line is either a _____ or an _____ .

26. The quarter-wave shorted section of a resonant line can be used as metallic _____ or _____ filters.

27. The quarter-wave shorted section of a resonant line has an impedance of _____ at one end and _____ at the other. This section can be used to _____ two widely different impedances.

28. The three basic losses in transmission lines are _____ , _____ , and _____ .

29. Wave propagation through the cavity of a wave guide is somewhat similar to propagation in _____ .

30. A transmitting antenna is an active device which _____ electromagnetic energy to free _____ .

31. The receiving antenna is a _____ device which has current induced into it by the passage of _____ waves.

32. Reversal of voltage polarities on and current direction through the antenna cause E and H fields to _____ and _____ .

33. Radiation is caused from the fact that a portion of the E and H fields is trapped in space each time the current _____ .

34. The wave front travels out from the antenna at the rate of _____ miles per second, expanding as it goes.

35. The E lines travel _____ to the radiating antenna, and the H lines are _____ to the E lines.

36. The polarization of an antenna is its position relative to the _____ .

37. For best reception, the _____ of the transmitting and receiving antennas should be the same.

38. As the wave passes the receiving antenna, a current is induced into the antenna by _____ lines cutting across it.

39. A quarter-wave section of an antenna mounted vertical to a conducting surface will exhibit all the characteristics of a _____ antenna. This is a _____ antenna.

40. Antennas can be made directional by using _____ and _____ .

41. Sky waves are radiated at an upward angle and usually bounce back and forth between the _____ and the _____ . These waves are responsible for most of the reliable _____ _____ radio communications.

42. Ground waves are radiated downward and generally cover a range up to about _____ miles.

Responses for Section 8 Exercise

(1) 0.01. (2) Radiation. (3) Low power. (4) Shielded; coaxial.
(5) Wave guides. (6) Power; frequency. (7) Source; destination
(load). (8) RF amplifier; antenna. (9) Antenna; RF amplifier.
(10) L/C; E x I. (11) Infinitely long. (12) Delivered; used.

(13) Electric field; magnetic field. (14) Positive; negative; perpendicular. (15) Medium; frequency. (16) Wave length. (17) 186,000 miles; wave length. (18) Medium; space. (19) Source; load. (20) Resonant. (21) Reflected. (22) Parallel resonant. (23) Series resonant. (24) Reflected short; reflected open. (25) Capacitor; inductor. (26) Insulators; harmonic. (27) Zero; infinity; match. (28) Copper, dielectric, and radiation. (29) Space. (30) Couples; space. (31) Passive; electromagnetic. (32) Build up; decay. (33) Reverses direction. (34) 186,000. (35) Parallel; perpendicular. (36) Earth's surface. (37) Polarity. (38) H. (39) Half-wave; Marconi. (40) Reflectors; directors. (41) Ionosphere; earth's surface; long range. (42) 75.

EXERCISE FOR SECTION 9
Devices With Special Applications

1. Solid state resistors are based on the fact that semiconductors are sensitive to _____ changes.

2. The thermistor is a solid state resistor with a _____ temperature coefficient. It may be used to detect _____ changes in temperature.

3. The photoresistor is a _____ sensitive resistor.

4. The varistor registers a rapid decrease in resistance when the _____ of the applied voltage changes.

5. The variable capacitance diode is used as a _____ sensitive capacitor.

6. A diode which operates at avalanche breakdown in either direction is the _____ .

7. A tunnel diode has an extended operation area where its current is _____ proportional to voltage.

8. Silicon rectifier packages can be obtained to meet any reasonable requirement of _____ and _____ .

9. A silicon controlled rectifier is actually a four layer _____ .

10. The photodiode produces a reverse current which is directly proportional to _____ .

11. Power transistors use larger than normal elements and employ special techniques for _____ .

12. Three transistors that have less collector to base capacitance than most transistors are the _____ , the _____ , and the _____ .

13. Reducing the collector to base capacitance enables transistors to operate at _____ .

14. A cryosar is a semiconductor _____ which operates in _____ _____ temperatures.

15. The solar cell is a small semiconductor device which converts light energy directly into _____ .

16. Masers were developed in an effort to reduce _____ and _____ in high frequency amplifiers.

17. The _____ frequency of the maser raises the energy level of a confined group of atoms.

18. The signal to be amplified by the maser _____ the energized atoms back to their normal level.

19. As the energized atoms in the maser drop back to a normal energy level, they _____ energy which is _____ by the signal.

20. The maser is a very effective amplifier of _____ frequencies.

21. The laser is an effective amplifier of _____ frequencies.

22. Lasers can carry large quantities of information on a single _____ beam.

Responses for Section 9 Exercise

(1) Temperature. (2) Negative; small. (3) Light. (4) Amplitude. (5) Voltage. (6) Symmetrical zener. (7) Inversely. (8) Voltage; current. (9) Switch. (10) Light intensity. (11) Heat dissipation. (12) Intrinsic; tetrode; field effect. (13) Higher frequencies. (14) Switch; super cold. (15) Usable voltage. (16) Noise; transit time. (17) Pumping. (18) Triggers. (19) Release; absorbed. (20) Microwave. (21) Light. (22) Light.

INDEX

INDEX

C

M

N